Theme Drama

*40 Bible—based sketches
and dramatic ideas for use
with 8 to 13 year olds*

Compiled by Marina Brown

Scripture Union

Scripture Union, 207–209 Queensway,
Bletchley, MK2 2EB, England.
© Scripture Union 2000

First published 2000

ISBN 1 85999 436 9

*With grateful thanks to all the writers
who have contributed to* SALT 8 to 10+
and SALT 11 to 13+. *Without their hard
work and creativity, this book could
not have been produced.*

The right of Marina Brown to be identified as
author of the Introduction and compiler of this
work has been asserted by her in accordance
with the Copyright, Designs and Patents Act
1988.

Scripture quotations are from the
Contemporary English Version ©American
Bible Society 1991, 1992, 1995. Used by
permission/Anglicisations © British & Foreign
Bible Society 1997.

We have made every effort to identify the
authors of the material in this book. If, however,
we have failed to attribute some material
correctly please inform us and we will rectify
this in any future editions.

British Library Cataloguing-in-Publication Data
A catalogue record for this book is available
from the British Library.

Design by Blue Pig Design Co.
Cover illustration by Blue Pig Design Co.
Internal illustrations by Mike Kazybrid

Printed and bound in Malta by Interprint.

Contents

OLD TESTAMENT

Introduction 4

In the beginning, God… 6
Lots of action 8
All God's plan 9
The king acts 11
Walk through story 12
David, the giant-killer! 14
On the run 15
They're gone 16
Elijah finds God 17
P-R-O-P-H-E-T 19
A circular drama 20
Manasseh changes 21
Going potty! 22
Fired up! 23
Nehemiah builds a wall 24
A job well done! 25

NEW TESTAMENT

Get ready for Jesus 26
Words of hope 27
What a surprise! 28
On the record 29
Crossed lines 30
The big fight 31
Follow the Leader 33
Zebedee phones home 35
There's some wine in my bucket! 36
The perfect prayer 38
Two a penny 39
Shocking! 40
Sheep tales 41
Sidney Spender, Super Spender 42
Wait till I tell you! 44
Malchus' miracle 46
What a scoop! 48
Gumpole of the Bailey 49
Rockety Rock 51
Instant pose 53
Foiled again! 54
Jigsaw tale 55
A red letter day 57
Trouble on site 58

Index of titles 60
Index of themes 60
Index of Bible passages 61

Other resources from Scripture Union 62

Introduction

Background

For those who think that drama is some new, maybe rather desperate, way to convey biblical truths it should come as a salutary reminder that the church has from earliest times used story, art and drama as teaching – and entertainment – media: Jesus himself was the master storyteller, early churches had their interior walls richly decorated with picture stories, and the medieval mystery plays are prime examples of how drama can be used effectively to teach and entertain. All these methods were adopted for audiences with little individual access to Scripture.

The aim of this book

Today we find ourselves in what has been sometimes described as a non-book culture – a culture where other forms of media communication are taking over the ground previously occupied by the printed word. While we may dispute that, it is nevertheless true that the world of the Bible is far removed from present-day culture and is largely an unknown territory for many young people.

In an attempt to bridge this chasm, writers of the Scripture Union *SALT* materials for church children's groups, have often turned to drama as a means of communicating biblical truths in an arresting, amusing and relevant way. Familiar passages often take on a new intensity and immediacy when role-played and seen from the point of view of a participant or spectator. Because this work is freshly commissioned for each quarterly magazine, much of it can easily be used once and then lost for the future. This book is an attempt to put that right by gathering together a wide variety of tried and tested sketches and dramatic ideas covering the Old and New Testaments.

Content

The majority of the material in the present volume first appeared in Scripture Union's *SALT 8 to 10+* and *SALT 11 to 13+* materials between the years 1996 and 1999, but we have also commissioned some brand new scripts especially for this publication.

We have included a broad range of biblical material from both Old and New Testaments, including groups of dramas for the special festivals of Christmas and Easter.

The Old Testament selection includes some well-known stories with a new presentational twist. The life and teachings of Jesus in the New Testament are well represented, as is the early church.

There are a range of approaches including both scripted and unscripted dramas. The unscripted material will, we hope, allow you to have a go at more impromptu styles of drama and encourage you to apply the methods shown to adapt passages of Scripture for, and with, your group.

Some dramas may need adult participation or a mix of adults and young people. Others involve every member of the group in some way.

When can I use this book?

The dramas have a wide range of uses beyond the groups for which they were originally intended. Mid-week clubs and school Christian Union groups are obvious examples, as are church holiday clubs or groups who are having a weekend away together. They could also form a useful part of the teaching at Christian holidays, school missions and assemblies.

Some would also be ideal for use during all-age services. Because their original target audience was in the late primary/early secondary school age they are neither too difficult for younger children nor too childish for adults. We have indicated where sketches or dramatic ideas would be most appropriate with either 8 to 10-year olds (look for the * symbol) or 11 to 13-year olds (look for the † symbol) but not across the whole age range.

The uses for this book are therefore as wide as imagination and opportunity allow!

How to use this book

To help you decide if a drama is for you, a simple set of icons has been devised which will show you at a glance how many actors are required and whether scripts or props are needed.

 scripted

 unscripted

 props needed

 no props needed

 number of actors required

There is also a title index, a theme index including major Christian festivals, and a Bible passage index at the back for easy reference.

Using drama

A few simple guidelines will help to make using drama a happy experience and a useful tool.

Start with something simple, straightforward and well within the capabilities of your group, such as dramatised reading or choral speaking, to help them gain confidence. Warm up first so that people don't strain their muscles or their voices. Use games to get the group moving around the space and perhaps have some fun with tongue-twisters and songs to get their vocal cords warmed up.

Perhaps use a simple technique like saying aloud a phrase such as 'What a lovely day!', asking the group to emphasise a different word each time or express a different emotion – joy, sadness, happiness. Have fun with this! This kind of activity will help your group put life into their reading.

Remember that scripted drama needs preparation. If you intend public performance, the scripts should ideally be learned and well rehearsed. At the very least, the participants must read over their scripts aloud together beforehand.

Don't force anyone to take part – some children and adults will be reluctant, so respect this.

Be wise in your choice – some dramas like role-plays are not intended for public performance but are ideal for group use. Some involving the whole group could allow shy children effectively to lose themselves and their inhibitions in the crowd because of the unthreatening form of participation required.

All those involved in the production of this book trust that you will enjoy using it and find it a valuable tool in your ministry.

In the beginning, God...

JUDITH MERRELL  4

Bible base: Genesis 1,2

Cast

BERT BOFFIN: a bright and brainy quiz show host.
FRANK FAX: an intellectual type, who can look up the answer to any question.
PETE AND PAM PARKER: two members of the studio audience.

Props: three bar stools; a table; lots of reference books and Bibles.

The scene is a television studio. Three bar stools or chairs are arranged in a semi-circle for Bert, Pam and Pete. There is a library corner consisting of a table piled high with an impressive assortment of reference books, and a space in the middle for Frank to sit.

FRANK: As usual, our question comes from the studio audience. So, let's ask Pete and Pam Parker to pop up here and pose their question!
BERT : Hi Pete! Hi Pam! *(Shaking hands)* Welcome to the show. Perhaps we should call you a right pair of nosy Parkers!
PAM: *(Giggling)* Err thanks!
BERT: Right, take a seat and tell us your brainteaser. *(Bert, Pete and Pam take seats, while Frank goes over to the library corner and perches on a table where he is surrounded by huge piles of books which he continually consults.)*
PETE: OK, here's our question… *(Reading from question card)* How did it all start?
BERT: How did what all start?
PAM: Us, the world… everything, you know!
FRANK: Oh, you mean creation!
PETE: Exactly! How did we create this world where we're living?
FRANK: We didn't. God did.
PAM: How do you know that?
FRANK: *(Selecting a Bible)* It says so in the Bible. Listen *(Reading from NIV Bible)* 'In the beginning God…'
PETE: In the beginning God… what?
FRANK: Don't you see? It's all there in those first four words, 'In the beginning God…' God was there right at the start. Before anything else existed God was there and he created everything else.

PETE: Go on…
FRANK: *(Reading)* 'In the beginning God created the heavens and the earth.' It's all here in chapter 1, verse 1 of Genesis, the very first book in the Bible.
PAM: What about us? When did he create people?
PETE : Surely he created us first?
FRANK: No, he couldn't just create people and leave us floating about in nothing. He needed to create somewhere for us to live first.
PAM: OK! So what did he make first?
FRANK: In the beginning everything was a dark, swirling, surging, seething watery mass, so God created light.
PAM: What do you mean?
PETE: Firelight or electric light?
BERT: He means daylight!
FRANK: That's right! God's new light separated day from night.
PETE: So what came next?
FRANK: *(Looking in Good News Bible)* A dome.
PAM: *(Amazed)* The Millennium Dome?
FRANK: *(Laughing)* No! *(Pointing to his Bible)* A special canopy which God called the sky. Then the Bible tells us that God commanded the water below the sky to come together in one place, so that land would appear.
PETE: And did the water listen?
FRANK: It certainly did!
BERT: The whole universe obeys God.
FRANK: *(Reading from encyclopaedia)* The sea now covers two thirds of the earth's surface, and land makes up the remaining third.'
BERT: So that's how we got the land and the sea.
PAM: And then God created you and me?
FRANK: Wrong! And then God covered the whole land with vegetation. *(Reading)* In fact, he created more than 400,000 different types of plants.
BERT: Roots and shoots
FRANK: And juicy fruit
BERT: And bright green leaves
FRANK: Becoming harvest sheaves.
BERT: You see, all the while God was preparing a special place for people to enjoy.
FRANK: So God created the sun to give us light in the daytime
BERT : And the moon and stars to provide light at night.

FRANK: *(Coming over to group with encyclopaedia)* Look at this! It's amazing! Here, Pete, you read it out.

PETE: *(Reading)* The sun is so far away from earth that it takes 8.3 minutes for its light to reach us! Well, I never knew that before!

PAM: Mind-blowing!

FRANK: Next, he put fish in the water and birds in the air.

BERT: From the lapwing to the lark

FRANK: From the shrimp to the shark

BERT: God created every single flying, floating, swimming thing!

FRANK: And he told them to increase and multiply.

BERT: And they did!

FRANK: Then God created animals *(returning to table and holding up encyclopaedia)*, and this book tells us that there are well over ten million different species!

BERT: Large and small,

FRANK: Short and tall,

PAM: God made them all?

FRANK: He did!

BERT: Cats, rats and gnats,

FRANK: Dogs and frogs,

BERT: And hairy warthogs!

FRANK: And he was pleased with everything that he had created.

BERT: Very pleased!

FRANK: But there was something missing.

PETE: What was that?

FRANK: God wanted someone to talk to.

BERT: So he decided to create human beings.

FRANK: He created man and woman in his own image. Adam and Eve were the first man and woman, but *(reading from an encyclopaedia)* today there are more than 5,000 million people on earth and that figure is expected to double in the next forty years.

PETE: So he created people last of all?

BERT: That's right, he created people as soon as the world that he had made was ready for them.

FRANK: Then, he gave them his creation and asked them to take care of it.

PAM: That's quite a responsibility!

FRANK: Finally, God sat back and looked at the world he had created and he was pleased with everything he saw.

BERT: And he rested after all his hard work.

FRANK: Well, Pete and Pam, *(standing up, as if to wind up the programme)*, does that answer your question?

PETE: *(Standing up and shaking hands)* It certainly does. Thank you!

PAM: *(Getting up)* But there's still one thing I don't understand…

BERT: And what's that?

PAM: How come people don't take better care of the wonderful world that God created and gave to us?

FRANK: That sounds like a question for our next programme!

BERT: Thank you for watching *Find the Facts.* Goodbye, and see you next week!

Lots of action

Bible base: Genesis 13, 14

You will need Bibles or copies of Genesis 13:1–18 and 14:1–16.

Divide the children into two groups. If you are the only leader, either stay with the younger/noisier children and let the older children work together, or delegate a child to lead each group, and go between the two.

Explain to both groups at once that they will need to read their passages and then make up a play, based on it, to show the other group. Ask one group to look at Genesis 13 and the other, Genesis 14. For chapter 14 it would help the children if you wrote a brief summary of verses 1 to 9, explaining that four kings were fighting five kings, and that the king of Lot's city was on the losing side.

Give the groups time to read the passages and then time to practise. When they are ready, ask them to show their drama.

When the dramas are complete, ask the children why they chose to present the story in that way and whether they all agreed. Then ask the groups about the choices that the characters in the story made.

All God's plan

DAVID BELL

Bible base: Genesis 37, 39–46

Cast

This is Your Life **PRESENTER**
JOSEPH (*One older Joseph and one young Joseph*)
 STEWARD
REUBEN
JUDAH
BENJAMIN
EIGHT OTHER BROTHERS (or combine parts to have four other brothers: 1/5, 2/6, 3/7, 4/8 or two: 1/3/5/7; 2/4/6/8).
KING'S SERVANT

Props and costumes: big red book; Joseph's decorated coat; Egyptian ruler's outfit; fancy cup; packed lunches; banquet (food could be mimed or shared with audience); signs saying 'In Egypt, some years later' and 'The next morning'.

Video flashback action takes place to one side of the *This is Your Life* stage.

(*Older Joseph and Presenter enter.*)
PRESENTER: Hello. Tonight, we're joining with family and friends, with video flashbacks, to say 'Joseph Zaphenath Paneah – this is your life!' (*Opening the big red book*) Born to parents Jacob and Rachel, you lived with your ten other brothers in Canaan…

Brothers 1–8, Reuben and Judah enter, holding younger Joseph. They 'throw' him into a pit (eg behind chairs, or out of a doorway). Reuben exits. Brothers 1–8 and Judah get out packed lunches and sit/stand roughly in the order they will speak.

JOSEPH: (*Off, repeated*) Let me out!
BROTHER 1: So how do we punish the nasty little sneak then, brothers?
BROTHER 2: Tarantulas? (*Picks one up.*)
JOSEPH: (*Off*) I want to go home!
BROTHER 3: Ah! Daddy's little diddums! Leave him to rot.
JOSEPH: (*Off*) You'll be sorry!
BROTHER 4: Still thinks he's better than us. Make him eat grass for a year.
BROTHER 5: You know Joseph's stuck-up dreams – well, let's give him nightmares. How about we smear honey all over his body, then we get some

extra big juicy ants from the far side of the valley and…
BROTHER 6: (*Interrupting*) I say knife him!
BROTHER 7: (*Pointing*) Phwooar, look at those Heavy Goods Camels. It's a mobile superstore.
JUDAH: That's it! Let's sell him.
JOSEPH: (*Off*) You know you'll all bow down to me one day!
BROTHER 8: Nice one, Judah!

PRESENTER: The next few years saw you living in some varied places. You got a job with one of Pharoah's officials, a Mr Potiphar, but had to leave in a hurry.
JOSEPH: Yes - unfortunately his wife accused me of attacking her, all because I refused to sleep with her. Of course it's now been proved that she was telling lies but it was all over the papers at the time and because I was only a slave, no one would believe my word against hers.
PRESENTER: So, in fact, the next few years saw you in jail for a crime you didn't commit. Here tonight, we've flown in an old friend from those days – a fellow prisoner, the king's personal servant…
KING'S SERVANT: Well, the most remarkable thing I remember from those days is that Joseph could interpret dreams. I was released two years earlier than Joseph and it wasn't until my master, the king, had a very alarming dream warning of a terrible famine, that I remembered that Joseph might be able to help and he was finally released. It was then that he was made an official in charge of food provisions for the whole country.
The servant goes and sits down.
PRESENTER: And from then on, things just got better and better for you!
JOSEPH: Yes, although I still missed my family, despite what my brothers did.
PRESENTER: So, when they appeared in Egypt some years later, in search of food, you were pleased to see them?
JOSEPH: Yes, of course, but I didn't let them know who I was at first. I wanted to see if my brothers had changed for the better. The first time they came, Benjamin, my youngest brother, wasn't with them so I made an excuse to keep Simeon in prison here to make sure that they came back again, bringing him with them.

Sign: 'In Egypt, some years later'.
Reuben and Benjamin enter. All the brothers stand in the order they will speak. The steward brings on banquet food. Joseph enters in rich clothes. The steward hands him his special cup.

JOSEPH: Welcome again, visitors! You come to buy more corn? How are you?

REUBEN: O great ruler, we are honoured. We bring gifts…

JOSEPH: And, er, Simeon is it? Have you enjoyed my prison?

BROTHER 1: I have been treated well, Lord Zaphenath Paneah.

JOSEPH: And your old father you told me of. Is he still alive?

BROTHER 2: Excellency, our father is well.

The brothers all bow down to Joseph.

JOSEPH: And is this your little brother? *(Touching Benjamin's head)* God bless you. *(Joseph rushes out, then returns calmer.)*

JOSEPH: Serve the food!

Steward serves; they sit and eat.

BROTHER 3: Thank you, Your Wonderfulness! Thank you, thank you!

JUDAH: You are too kind.

BROTHER 4: We're overwhelmed by your kindness.

BROTHER 5: Your kindness is as the great rushing waters of a river, as the mountains which stand high in the sky, as the wind swirling…

BROTHER 6: *(Interrupting)* Especially after last time.

BROTHER 7: And the muddle with the money.

BROTHER 8: We didn't steal it. Honest, boss!

BENJAMIN: Mmmm! I'm full!

JOSEPH: Now, time for bed. You set off early tomorrow.

All brothers exit. Joseph hands the steward his cup, pointing at Benjamin. Steward sneaks off.

Sign: 'The next morning'.
Enter all brothers with steward, who carries the cup. The brothers throw themselves on the ground before Joseph.

JOSEPH: What have you done?

JUDAH: Sir, we didn't steal the cup! But we are guilty men. God has shown you that.

JOSEPH: *(Pointing at Benjamin)* This man had the cup in his bag. He will be my slave.

JUDAH: Sir, it would kill my father. He has already lost one precious son, Joseph. Take me as your slave instead, and let him go home safely.

JOSEPH: *(To steward)* Leave us! *(Steward exits.)* I am Joseph! *(Stunned silence)* Don't blame yourselves for selling me as a slave. It was really God who sent me here to Egypt – to save lives.

All freeze, showing shocked/happy/scared reactions.

PRESENTER: So Joseph – how would you sum up your life?

JOSEPH: Well – I'd have to say that it's all been God's plan…

The king acts

MARY GREEN

Bible base: Exodus 1:1 – 2:10

Cast
OLD EGYPTIAN
KING
NARRATOR
SHIPRAH AND PUAH
BABY MOSES
AMRAM AND JOCHEBED (Moses' parents, named in Exodus 6:20)
MIRIAM (Moses' sister named in Exodus 15:20)
PRINCESS

Props: eleven copies of the script highlighted by parts; prompt lines for Egyptian and Israelite chorus, written on large pyramid blocks (see illustration); props and costumes (optional).

Ask two leaders or two older children to put up the words for the chorus. You could copy the pyramids onto large sheets of paper and cut out each section. Helpers hold up the appropriate section when it appears in the script, then fix to a wall or board with *Blu-tack*. Or fix the whole pyramids on the wall, cover with a sheet of black paper and raise the paper to reveal the line that is about to be spoken. Give helpers a copy of the script with the Egyptian or Israelite chorus parts highlighted.

Ask the children or leaders to read the parts. Apart from the narrator and the king, most have one or two lines. Highlight each part on separate scripts. Divide the other children into two groups. One group will be the Egyptians. Point out the leader/child who will be holding their lines. The other group will be the Israelites. Again point to their 'leader'. If necessary, the leader can say each set of lines first for the chorus to repeat.

OLD EGYPTIAN: (*Hobbling across the stage with a stick*) I remember Joseph... Israelite who kept us alive in the famine... family came to live here... good people... (*He hobbles off.*)
NARRATOR: One hundred years later.
KING: Israelites everywhere! What right have they got to be here? What if they become our enemies? What shall I do?
EGYPTIANS: Make them work. (*x2*)
NARRATOR: So the Israelites were put to work in the fields and on the building sites.

ISRAELITES: Work till we drop. (*x2*)
NARRATOR: But the mums kept having babies, and there were more and more Israelites in Egypt.
KING: Help! Israelites everywhere! What shall I do?
EGYPTIANS: Kill the boys. (*x2*)
NARRATOR: So the king called the Hebrew midwives who helped the mums give birth.
KING: Kill the boys, let the girls live!
SHIPRAH AND PUAH: What shall we do?
ISRAELITES: Fear God, not the king!
NARRATOR: ... and they let the baby boys live.
KING: Israelite boys everywhere! What have you been doing?
SHIPRAH: (*Very slowly*) The mums are so quick.
PUAH: The babies are there before we are.
KING: What shall I do with these baby boys?
EGYPTIANS: Throw them in the river! (*x2*)
NARRATOR: So the Egyptians did. But meanwhile, in Amram's house...
BABY: Waaaa. Waaaa.
AMRAM: It's a boy! What shall we do?
JOCHEBED: Leave it to me.
NARRATOR: The baby's mum hid him for three months. Then she got a basket, painted it with tar, put the baby in it and hid it in the rushes at the edge of the river.
ISRAELITES: (*As rushes*) Rustle, rustle.
MIRIAM: It's the princess!
NARRATOR: Fresh Nile water, good for the skin. Take off your crown and jump right... What's that?
BABY: Waaaaaaa. Waaaaaaaa.
PRINCESS: It's a baby!
EGYPTIANS AND ISRAELITES: Clever!
PRINCESS: An Israelite baby. What shall I do?
MIRIAM: Please ma'am, can I fetch a nurse? (*Aside*) I know who I'll fetch!
PRINCESS: Oh yes! Now what shall I call him?
ISRAELITES AND EGYPTIANS: MOSES!

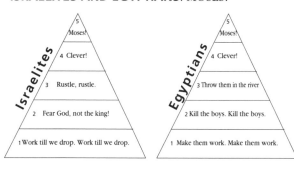

Walk
through story*

JUDITH MERRELL

Bible base: Exodus 12:21–36; 13:17 – 14:31

Props: pitta bread, cold lamb or other Passover food; herbs or horseradish on a plate; tomato ketchup in a small bowl; a leafy twig; a selection of outdoor clothes; 'cloud' and 'fire' painted backgrounds; 'the sea' made from large pieces of wallpaper lining paper joined together and painted blue; walking stick.

You will need to have read Exodus 12:21–36, 13:17 – 14:31 beforehand. Tell the story in your own words. A possible outline is given. When they are not moving round the room, ask the children to sit for the next part of the story.

The Israelites were slaves in Egypt for many years, but the king refused to let them leave, even after God sent many terrible things, like millions of frogs, flies, or locusts. Eventually Moses warned the king that the last disaster would be more terrible than all the others. At midnight on a certain date the first-born son in each Egyptian family would die. Once again the king took no notice.

The Israelites got precise instructions to follow so that their children would be protected. They had to prepare a meal with bitter herbs, roast lamb and bread made without yeast. They had to eat it in outdoor clothes to show that they were ready to leave. Some blood from the lamb had to be painted on the doorpost of the house so that God's angel

would know an Israelite family lived there, and would 'pass over' that house. *Give a child tomato ketchup and a leafy twig, to daub on the doorpost. (Make sure you wash it off later!) With their coats on, let them sample part of the Passover meal, eg pitta bread or cold lamb. Let them sniff the herbs.*

Sure enough, at midnight on the appointed date, the first-born son in each Egyptian house died. The king called Moses and Aaron and told them to get out. The Egyptians gave the Israelites gold, silver and clothes and begged them to go quickly. Six hundred thousand Israelite men, plus the women and the children left Egypt that day. God guided them with a pillar of cloud in the day and a pillar of fire at night. *A child walks in front holding up the cloud/fire, and leads the group around the room.*

It wasn't long before the king realised he'd lost his entire slave workforce. He summoned his best chariot regiment and sent them off to bring the people back. By this time the Israelites had reached the edge of the Red Sea. They were very frightened when they saw the chariots behind them and started to moan to Moses that they should have stayed in Egypt. Moses told them not to be afraid because the Lord who rescued them from Egypt would save them now.

That night, God's pillar of cloud stopped the Egyptians seeing where the Israelites were. God told Moses to hold his stick out over the Red Sea. All night the wind blew, pushing back the water and making a dry path through the sea.

Ask a child to hold up a stick over the 'sea' you have painted. Tear the sea down the centre and roll it back to make a pathway through. The children cross from one side to the other.

When the Egyptians tried to follow, the water rolled back and the whole army was drowned. The Israelites saw God's amazing power and praised and worshipped him for helping them.

Conclude by singing a lively praise song.

David, the giant-killer!

JUDITH MERRELL

Bible base: 1 Samuel 17:1-58

Cast
GOLIATH
DAVID
ISRAELITE ARMY
PHILISTINE ARMY

This sketch is very simple to learn since David and Goliath can read their text from clipboards and the two armies simply echo the last line spoken by their leader. David should stand on one side, with the Israelites assembled in regimental ranks just behind. On the opposite side, Goliath should stand on a block to give him greater height, with the Philistine army grouped close by. The two armies should deliver their lines loudly and enthusiastically, copying the style and mannerisms from David and Goliath.

GOLIATH: I'm Goliath, the secret weapon of the Philistine army. (*Climbing onto a block*) I'm nearly three metres tall.

PHILISTINES: (*Punching air enthusiastically like a group of football fans*) He's nearly three metres tall. Yeah!

DAVID: I'm David, the youngest of Jesse's sons. Three of my brothers are soldiers, but I'm only a shepherd boy.

ISRAELITES: (*Shaking heads sadly*) He's only a shepherd boy!

GOLIATH: My armour alone weighs nearly fifty-seven kilos. It will protect me from ab- so-lute-ly anything.

PHILISTINES: It will protect him from ab-so-lute-ly anything.

DAVID: When I told the king that I wanted to fight, he was rather doubtful. Finally he offered to lend me his own armour. But it was much too big and I couldn't walk a step.

ISRAELITES: He couldn't walk a step.

DAVID: I've decided not to bother with armour. I'll have my shepherd's stick and my sling, that'll do for me. Oh yes, and I need five smooth stones.

ISRAELITES: (*Puzzled*) Five smooth stones?

GOLIATH: (*To Israelites*) Right then, you pathetic little scaredy-cats - have you found someone who'll dare to fight me?

PHILISTINES: Have you found someone who'll dare to fight him?

GOLIATH: I challenge your whole army! Remember, if your soldier wins, we will all become your slaves, but if we win, you must become our slaves.

PHILISTINES: Yes! You must become our slaves!

DAVID: I won't listen to you insult God's army any longer. I'll fight you! I'm not scared!

ISRAELITES: He's not scared!

GOLIATH: You! What a joke! You're only a little lad, an urchin, a cheeky brat. Why, I'll feed your body to the birds and animals!

PHILISTINES: He'll feed your body to the birds and animals.

DAVID: You're going to fight me with a sword, a spear and a javelin, but I'm going to fight you in the name of the Lord Almighty, the God of Israel. Our God will put every one of you in our power, and then I'll give *your* bodies to the birds and animals!

ISRAELITES: (*Without much confidence*) He'll give your bodies to the birds and animals.

GOLIATH: Ha ha ha! We'll see about that!

PHILISTINES: (*Splitting their sides*) We'll see about that!

DAVID: (*Miming the actions as he speaks*) With just one stone in my sling, like so, I whirl it above my head like this, let go and POW! Goliath is hit, smack between the eyes. Yes! Goliath is dead! God has given us the victory!

ISRAELITES: (*Amazed*) God has given us the victory!

DAVID: The Philistines are running away! Hallelujah!

ISRAELITES: Hallelujah!

DAVID: Thank you, God!

ISRAELITES: Thank you, God!

On the run [†]

LYNDA NEILANDS

Bible base: 1 Samuel 21:10 - 22:4

Cast
NARRATOR
DAVID
KING ACHISH
SERVANTS OF KING ACHISH
SUPPORTERS OF DAVID

NARRATOR: Things have gone badly wrong for David. King Saul wants to kill him, so now he's on the run. (*David runs on, looking anxiously over his shoulder. He sounds out of breath.*)

NARRATOR: He runs to the enemy city of Gath.

DAVID: At least I'll be safe from Saul, amongst his enemies.

NARRATOR: There, he gets spotted...

DAVID: Oh no! As if things weren't bad enough already, I've got spots.

NARRATOR: I didn't say 'spots', I said 'spotted'! There, he gets spotted by the servants of Achish, the king of Gath.

SERVANTS: (*Marching up to David*) We know who you are. You're David, the great Israelite warrior.

DAVID: You can forget the great Israelite warrior bit. I'm on the run. Saul's trying to kill me.

SERVANTS: (*Grabbing him*) Forget the warrior bit? Not likely. We've a little saying here, 'Saul has killed thousands of our people, but David has killed tens of thousands.' We're taking you to King Achish.

NARRATOR: This gives David a nasty feeling.

DAVID: What if King Achish looks for revenge? What if he takes me prisoner? Ohhhh, I wish I'd never come here. My stomach is churning. My mouth is dry. My legs feel like jelly.

NARRATOR: In other words, David is scared witless.

DAVID: (*Trembling*) I admit it. I'm scared witless. Hey, wait a minute... that gives me an idea.

NARRATOR: It strikes David that one way to get round King Achish would be to pretend he has lost his wits.

Enter King Achish.

SERVANTS: Look what we've got here, Your Majesty. It's David, the great Israelite warrior who killed tens of thousands of our people. He's on the run from King Saul.

DAVID: (*Pretends to be a dog.*) Woof... woof...

woof...

SERVANTS: What's got into him?

DAVID: Grrrrrr.

KING ACHISH: Haven't I got enough madmen around me already, without you bringing another one into the house?

NARRATOR: The plan pays off. David escapes from Gath and finds a new hide-out in Adullam's Cave. He's still on the run, but now as well as feeling scared, he feels humiliated. I mean, what a comedown!

DAVID: A few months ago I had it all - fame, popularity, a brilliant future - and now look at me: I've lost everything and my life is in danger.

NARRATOR: In spite of this, deep down, David knows he's not alone.

DAVID: (*Kneeling*) Have pity, God Most High! My enemies chase me all day. Many of them are pursuing and attacking me, but even when I am afraid I keep on trusting you.

NARRATOR: Before long, God sends him company. His brothers and the rest of his family join him in the cave. Other people come too and soon David is the leader of 400 men.

SUPPORTERS: We're with you, David. You can count on us.

NARRATOR: Of course, David still has his bad days, days when his stomach churns and his mouth goes dry and his legs turn to jelly. But when fear wells up, he deals with it.

DAVID: When I pray, Lord God, my enemies will retreat, because I know for certain that you are with me. I praise your promises! I trust you and am not afraid. No one can harm me.

NARRATOR: No prizes for guessing the end of the story. David doesn't get killed. Instead, he becomes king in Saul's place. (*David stands up as the narrator puts a crown on his head.*) It's a big relief for him not to be on the run any more.

DAVID: Phew!

NARRATOR: But he has learned some important lessons from those days when he feared for his life.

DAVID: God used them to strengthen my faith.

They're gone

HEATHER BELL

Bible base: 2 Samuel 1:1–27

Cast
NARRATOR
MESSENGER
DAVID
CROWD

Props: copies of the script, cue card or OHP with words and actions of the crowd (see uppercase words in script).

Recap on the story of David so far: King Saul tried to kill David, who had to run away. Helped by Jonathan, David ran to enemy country, then to a cave in his own country. Saul kept chasing David, and twice David could have killed Saul, but he wouldn't. David was finally given land in enemy country, and thought he had some good news. Perform the drama with some children reading the individual parts, and everyone joining in the crowd scenes. Ask a helper with a script to show the children their cues.

NARRATOR: Good news! The families of David and his men had been captured, but David and his men raided the Amalekites and brought them back. They're celebrating now…

CROWD: PARTY NOISES.

Into the party runs a tired messenger, clothes torn, head and clothes covered in soil.

CROWD: SUDDENLY SILENT.

DAVID: What's happened?

MESSENGER: The army of Israel has been attacked by the Philistines and been defeated. Many were killed. Worse – Saul and his three sons have been killed.

CROWD: OH NO!

DAVID: How do you know?

MESSENGER: I was with the Israelites. I saw King Saul badly wounded and about to be captured. He asked me to kill him. So I did. Here is his crown and his armband.

NARRATOR: This wasn't true. Saul had killed himself, but the messenger thought David would be pleased.

CROWD: GASPS.

DAVID: How dare you kill your king? You deserve to die. Kill him!

Messenger falls to ground.

NARRATOR: David and his men were sad for the whole of that day, and wouldn't eat.

CROWD AND DAVID: CRYING AND LOOKING SAD.

DAVID: I have written a song for everyone in Israel to learn, to remind us of this terrible day. It tells of the bravery of Saul and Jonathan and their men. They were swifter than eagles and stronger than lions. Israel was rich because of them. And Jonathan, my closest friend… (*Voice trails off.*)

NARRATOR: So everyone learned David's song: 'Israel, your famous hero lies dead on the hills,

CROWD: 'ISRAEL, YOUR FAMOUS HERO LIES DEAD ON THE HILLS,

NARRATOR: … and your mighty warriors have fallen.'

CROWD: … AND YOUR MIGHTY WARRIORS HAVE FALLEN.'

Elijah finds God

CLIVE DE SALIS

Bible base: 1 Kings 19:1-15

Cast
ELIJAH
ANGEL
NARRATOR
THE VOICE OF GOD

Props: a large broom (see note below); a mug of water; some cake; a large piece of bendable hardboard; twelve, or more, smooth round pebbles; one, or more, pairs of sticks; a torch (or several); red, orange and yellow tissue paper; cardboard; sticky tape.

Organise the children into teams to provide the following special effects:

1 Earthquake: a small group using a large piece of flexible hardboard to provide the sound–effect for the earthquake. The team split in two and the hardboard is held between them, one team at each end. The team bend and flex the hardboard to make a loud rumbling noise.

2 Wind: a larger team make the sound of the strong, blowing wind.

3 Rocks: a small team bang pieces of wood together to make loud cracking noises as the wind splits the rocks.

4 Extra sound effects: a small team have some large, smooth pebbles that they roll on a wooden floor or around a tabletop. This sound effect is used both during the earthquake and during the wind splitting the rocks.

5 A group of three children provide the fire effect. Beforehand, make a large cardboard frame and stretch a sheet of yellow tissue across it. Cut out and stick a few red and orange flame shapes (not too many or the light won't show through!) onto it. Dim the lights and have the children move torches around behind the tissue paper, to suggest flames flickering.

Tip: If you have a small group of children, teams three and four above can simultaneously provide the wind noise of team two. Team three can double as team one and team four can double up to do both team four's and team five's work.

Enter Elijah looking worried. In the far (back) corner one of the children is holding a broom upside down (the tip of the handle touching the floor).

ELIJAH: It's OK for you lot, looking comfortable as if there's not too much to worry about - well, I've had a whole bucketful of trouble these last few days. First, I show a whole bunch of Queen Jezebel's prophets of Baal who is the real God and now she is mad - she's more than angry with me - she's going to kill me. You might think I'm overdoing it but that woman has a temper. It's the way she screams at you *'Eeeeliiijjaaahhh – I'm going to kill you!'* and even her scream feels like death. Well, I didn't wait for the rest - I got out of there fast. So, here I am running for my life. Don't know where I'm going - just so long as it's a long way from her!

Elijah moves on a little and tells the audience more.

ELIJAH: First, my servant and I both got to Beersheba, but my servant couldn't keep up so I left him there. Oh, don't worry about him, it's me she's after - I'm the one she wants. I've been travelling all day and I'm well into the wilderness here, the very edge of the desert, and I need shelter.

Elijah sees the broom.

ELIJAH: At last, look, a broom tree, some shelter for me.

Elijah goes over and sits down under the broom (tree).

ELIJAH: That's it; I can't run any further. I've had enough, Lord, just let me die! I'm no better off than my ancestors!

Elijah lies down and goes to sleep.

NARRATOR: So Elijah lay down in the shade of the broom tree and slept.

An angel enters with a mug of water and some cake.

NARRATOR: After Elijah had slept for a while, God sent an angel to take Elijah some cake to eat and some water to drink.

The angel puts the mug and cake down in front of Elijah. Elijah wakes up and sees the food and drink.

ANGEL: Get up and eat.

Elijah drinks the water and eats a piece of the cake but is so tired he falls back to sleep. The angel takes the mug and cake, and leaves.

NARRATOR: Elijah was still too tired. He fell back to

sleep. After a while the angel returned with some more water and cake.

The angel enters with a mug of water and some cake and wakes up Elijah.

ELIJAH: What? What is it?

ANGEL: Get up and eat, or else you'll get too tired to travel.

Elijah sits up.

ELIJAH: Travel?

ANGEL: Yes, travel.

Elijah drinks the water and eats the piece of cake.

NARRATOR: The food and water made him strong enough to walk for forty days.

The angel takes the mug and leaves the stage. Elijah starts walking. The broom tree silently leaves the stage.

NARRATOR: Finally, Elijah came to the region of Sinai, to Horeb, God's mountain. There he found a cave in which to stop for the night.

Elijah lies down to sleep and, after a short pause, he wakes up again.

NARRATOR: In the morning, God's word came to Elijah.

VOICE OF GOD: Elijah, what are you doing here?

Elijah gets up and starts to reply calmly but becomes increasingly agitated as he explains to God the reason why he is there.

ELIJAH: Lord God All-Powerful, I've always done my best to obey you... And, Lord God Almighty, I've always served you – you alone. But your people have broken their covenant with you, they've broken their solemn promise to you. They've torn down your altars and killed all your prophets, except me! I am the only one left. *And now they're even trying to kill me! They're trying to kill me!*

VOICE OF GOD: Go out of the cave and stand on the mountain. I am going to pass by the mountain.

Elijah takes a few steps forward (outside the cave on the mountainside).

NARRATOR: So Elijah stood outside on the mountain and watched, but he saw nothing. But, as he waited, he heard the sound of a wind that grew stronger.

Sound effect of the wind.

NARRATOR: It grew so strong that it split the rocks.

The sound effect of the wind gets very loud and sound effects three and four are added. After a while all the sounds suddenly stop.

NARRATOR: But God was not in the wind. (*Pause*) Then Elijah heard and felt an earthquake beneath his feet.

Sound effect one begins, to which sound effect four is then added. After a while all the sounds suddenly stop.

NARRATOR: But God was not in the earthquake. (*Pause*) Then Elijah saw a fire.

Special effect five is used and then stops.

NARRATOR: But God was not in the fire. (*Pause*) And then there was silence.

Absolute silence from everyone.

NARRATOR: And God was there – in the silence. (*Pause*) And God whispered to Elijah…

VOICE OF GOD: (*Quietly*) Elijah, what are you doing here?

Elijah replies nervously, but more calmly.

ELIJAH: Lord God All-Powerful, I've always done my best to obey you... And, Lord God Almighty, I've always served you – you alone. But your people have broken their covenant with you; they've broken their solemn promise to you. They've torn down your altars and killed all your prophets, except me! I am the only one left, and now they are trying to kill me.

VOICE OF GOD: Elijah, I am the Lord your God, the Holy One of Israel and you are mine. I have work for you. Go back to the wilderness and go to Damascus. I have work for you.

Elijah leaves the stage as the narrator is speaking.

NARRATOR: So Elijah went back to the wilderness and on to Damascus and did everything God told him to do. And God was with Elijah – all the time.

Note: A number of versions of the Bible say that it is a broom tree except for the CEV and GNB. However we have used CEV and GNB for almost all of the narrative so that any child following the story in their Bibles can find the words directly in what they hear.

P-R-O-P-H-E-T

ANITA HAIGH

Bible base: 1 Kings 18:16-46; 2 Kings 5;
Daniel 2,4,5; Jonah 1-3

The chorus is chanted like an army marching song,
while the verses are spoken as a rhyme or rap.
Alternatively, the verses could be done as an army
chant with a leader chanting each line, and
everybody repeating it. Words in bold indicate first
beat in the bar.

Chorus:
P-R-O-**P**-**H**-E-T!
Find out what it **means** to be
A **mouth**piece of Al**might**y God.
Let's hear what **Elijah** did.

Verse 1:
Well, **he** was angry **with** the king
For **all** his idol-**worship**ping
He **gathered** all the **priests** of Baal
'I'll **show** who's God in **Israel**'.
Baal's **prophets** tried to **call** down fire
By **screaming** loud and **jumping** higher.
But **Elijah** called **upon** God's name,
And **down** from heaven came **fiery** flames.
The **people** fell face **down** with fear,
'We **know** the Lord our **God** is here!'
Elijah bowed **before** the Lord
For **he** had proved his **every** word.

Chorus:
P-R-O-**P**-**H**-E-T!
Find out what it **means** to be
A **mouth**piece of Al**might**y God.
Let's hear what **Elisha** did.

Verse 2:
Naaman was a **valiant** man
An **army** general **in** Aram.
But **he** was sick with **leprosy**
And **needed** help quite **urgently**.
His **wife's** maidservant **said** to him,
'**Elisha** would soon **cure** your skin.'
So **Naaman** left to **seek** a cure:
'**Elisha**, please make **my** skin pure?'
'Go **wash** in the Jordan **seven** times!
And your healing **you** will find!'
Naaman did as **he** was told,
And **trusted** in **Elisha's** God!

Chorus:
P-R-O-**P**-**H**-E-T!
Find out what it **means** to be
A **mouth**piece of Al**might**y God.
Let's find out what **Daniel** did.

Verse 3:
Now, **he** interpret**ed** the dreams
Of **many** rich and **powerful** kings.
He **told** King Neb what **one** dream meant
And **finally** got him **to** repent.
He was driven **from** his throne
'Til **he** admitted **he** was wrong!
His **son**, Belshazzar, **was** corrupt
And **did** not show the **Lord** respect.
A **ghostly** hand wrote **on** his wall
And **made** him choke and his **knees** wobble.
'**Daniel**', he asked, 'What **can** this mean?'
And **Dan** said, 'You're no **longer** king!'

Chorus:
P-R-O-**P**-**H**-E-T!
Find out what it **means** to be
A **mouth**piece of Al**might**y God.
Let's hear now what **Jonah** did.

Verse 4:
Now **Jonah** wasn't **keen** to be
A **prophet** of the **Lord**, you see.
To **Nineveh** he **had** to go,
But **he** had told the **Lord**, 'Oh no!
I'd **rather** take a **sailing** trip!'
And **so** he got on **board** a ship.
But **God** was cross and **sent** a storm.
The **crew** told Jonah, '**You're** to blame!'
Then they threw him **over** the rail,
But he **ended** up **inside** a whale.
The **whale** was sick on **Nineveh** beach,
So **Jonah** gave in and **began** to preach!

Chorus:
P-R-O-**P**-**H**-E-T!
Find out what it **means** to be
A **mouth**piece of Al**might**y God.
Could **you** do what **these** guys did?

A circular drama*

ANNE BRINICOMBE

Bible base: 2 Chronicles 24:1-16

Sit in a circle with a space in the middle as an acting area. Explain that together you are going to act out the life of King Joash. You will tell the story. Moving round clockwise from you, every time you mention a new character, the next person in the circle should stand up and join in the action as that character. Make sure that you pause to allow them time to act out the story. At the end of each scene, you will tell everyone to sit down. The process then starts again with the next child in the circle, so that the characters are played by different children in each scene. When 'the people' are mentioned, everyone should join in the action. You could use a large empty box as a prop. If you have a small group, go round the group more than once. If you have a large group, you can go through the story twice.

Scene 1: Joash was only seven years old when his uncle, Jehoiada the priest, placed a crown on his head and handed him a copy of the law to show that now Joash was king of Judah. As he sat on his throne, Joash listened to Jehoiada's advice, and Jehoiada helped him make decisions. Joash did what pleased God. Jehoiada even chose two wives for Joash. (*Sit down.*)

Scene 2: Now, at this time, the temple in Jerusalem was in a mess. Queen Athaliah had been a particularly bad queen. She had encouraged the people to use God's temple to worship the false god, Baal. They had bowed down and prayed to idols. They had damaged the temple and spoilt many of the special things there. (*Sit down.*)

Scene 3: King Joash was sad that the temple was in such a mess. So he decided to get it repaired. To do this he needed money, so the king called the priests and Levites (*two or three children*) to go round the country and collect money from the people – just like the tax which had been collected many years earlier. But the priests and Levites didn't do it straightaway; they were too busy in the temple. When Joash noticed that the money hadn't been collected, he called in Jehoiada and asked him why it hadn't been done. (*Sit down.*)

Scene 4: Then King Joash had an idea. He ordered the Levites to get a box and place it at the entrance to the temple. Then they sent messengers throughout the country to announce that everyone should bring their special tax money to the temple. The people were pleased with this idea. They came with their money and put it in the box. (*Sit down.*)

Scene 5: Whenever the box was full, it was emptied by the royal secretary and one of the high priest's staff. They then put the box back in its place. King Joash and Jehoiada his uncle, the priest, gave the money to the men in charge of the repairs. They hired expert stonemasons, carpenters and metalworkers. All of them worked hard and they restored the temple so it was as good as new. (*Sit down.*)

Scene 6: So much money was collected that there was enough to make some special bowls for the temple as well. Joash listened to the good advice of Jehoiada, and chose to do what was pleasing to God, as long as his uncle lived. But later in his life, Joash started to listen to other advisers. Then he made a different choice: to stop following God's ways, and to worship other gods. (*Sit down.*)

Discussion starter:
At the end, ask the children why they think Joash made the choices he did.

Manasseh changes

ANGELA AND JAMES HEPWORTH

Bible base: 2 Chronicles 33:1-20

In this script the leader is in the role of the chief temple workman.

Props: an apron and tools would add to the effect; the king's orders could be written out on scrolled paper; cardboard boxes could be used in the building work.

LEADER: Right, everyone. This is the dawn shift on temple maintenance, as laid down by His Majesty, King Manasseh (or, as he's known to you and me, 'Him-What-Must-Be-Obeyed-Or-Else-Something-Grim-And-Gruesome-Might-Happen'). Right? Is everyone here? Builders? Stonemasons? Silversmiths? Painters? General shifters and movers? (*Point to the children, allocating each one a role.*) Now listen carefully. These are His Majesty's orders: (*Reads.*)
'I, King Manasseh, Great and Terrible King of all Judah, order my grim and grotty workers to:
1 build and decorate several altars to other gods and put them in the temple.
2 build and decorate altars so I can worship the stars, in the temple courtyard.
3 create a large statue to be worshipped in the temple.' Any questions?
Set the children to work at their tasks, using the furniture and any boxes.

Call the children together again, take off your apron and, 'out of role', ask:
'What do you think God thought about Manasseh's changes in the temple?'
After discussion, resume your role, or start again with *'Some time later the temple workers were sitting around on a very long lunch break...'*

LEADER: Gather round, everybody: orders from His Majesty, King Manasseh. As you know, he has just got back from Assyria. He had a nasty experience as a prisoner there. Do you know, those Assyrians even stuck a hook through his nose! He was made to look like a right idiot! Anyway, here are his new orders: (*Reads.*)
'I, King Manasseh, humble servant of the Lord God, order the Lord's greatly honoured workers to:
1 destroy, smash and pulverise all altars and images of other gods and the stars at present in the Lord's temple.
2 chuck all the aforementioned stuff out of the city.
3 repair the altar of the Lord God. The Lord God be praised.'
Right then. Any questions?
Set the children to dismantle the things they have made in the room.

Discussion starter:
Afterwards, ask the children what they think caused the change in Manasseh's orders. Look at 2 Chronicles 33: 12,13 together. Ask the children if they are surprised that God forgave Manasseh.

Going potty!

Bible base: Jeremiah 18:1–12

Cast

MARIA WALLABY, reporter. She can use a home-made microphone or simply mime using one. The person speaking the words of **LUCINDA LA POT** could be hidden, or her words could be recorded and played back on tape.

Props: a vase; a lump of clay or Plasticine on a table; microphone (see above).

MARIA: This is Maria Wallaby, reporting live from the pottery for (*name of your TV station*). I have with me that most beautiful vessel, Lucinda La Pot. Lucinda, you are incredibly beautiful. Have you always been like this?

LUCINDA: No, Maria, like my brother Toby Mud there, I started out as a lump of clay.

MARIA: Wow, that's some transformation! What happened?

LUCINDA: Well, I was taken from my family home, the bucket where Toby and I lived, and I was put on the potter's wheel. Suddenly, it began to spin around and just as I felt I'd either fly off or be sick, the potter's hands came down on me. It was all very gentle to begin with. He started to make me into something beautiful.

MARIA: As easy as that? Do you mean to say that there were no problems?

LUCINDA: Well, no, it wasn't that easy, Maria. In fact it was very painful. You see he was going to make me into a tall flower vase, but something went wrong. To tell you the truth, I wriggled about on the wheel. So then I went all wrong! I was a total mess! I had a hole all the way down my side.

MARIA: Oh! What did the potter do?

LUCINDA: He looked at me and shook his head sadly. What happened next was very, very painful and very embarrassing. The potter picked me up and squashed me back into a lump of clay. I was back where I started! My career as a vase was over. I could hear Toby chuckling in the bucket. You see, he was once nearly a wonderful water jar, but he wriggled on the wheel, too. And look at him, now!

MARIA: So what happened to you?

LUCINDA: To my amazement, the wheel started to spin again and, although I was a bruised wreck, I started to take shape in the skilful hands of the potter. The rest, as they say, is history. Here I am, lovely Lucinda La Pot: a testimony to the skill and patience of the potter. I wasn't left in the clay bin but was made beautiful, to be admired by all.

MARIA: Thank you, Lucinda. A truly amazing and moving story. Now, back to the studio.

Discussion starter:
Afterwards, explain that God told Jeremiah to watch a potter working at his wheel. There, he gave Jeremiah a warning and a promise for his people. Put up two signs, saying 'Warning' and 'Promise'. Read Jeremiah 18:5,6. Explain that, like the potter with his clay, God had a wonderful design for his people. But they spoiled it by worshipping other gods. God loved them and wanted them to change, so he warned them of the punishment that was coming. (Put the lump of clay by the 'Warning' sign.) He promised to forgive them if they came back to him. (Put the vase by the 'Promise' sign.)

Fired up!

MAX RAWLINGS AND JEAN MITCHELL

Bible base: Daniel 3:1-30

Cast
NEBUCHADNEZZAR
SHADRACH
MESHACH
ABEDNEGO
TWO COURT OFFICIALS
MUSICIANS (preferably actually playing instruments)
TWO NARRATORS

Props: copies of the script; Bibles; costumes; rolls of toilet paper; something to represent the golden statue.

NARRATOR 1: King Nebuchadnezzar ordered a gold statue to be built twenty-seven metres high and nearly three metres wide. He had it set up in Dura Valley near the city of Babylon, and he commanded his governors, advisors, treasurers, judges, and his other officials to come from everywhere in his kingdom to the dedication of the statue. So all of them came and stood in front of it (Daniel 3:1-3 CEV).
Statue is brought on and all gather round.
NARRATOR 2: An official said:
OFFICIAL 1: When you hear the music you gotta bow down.
NARRATOR 2: So, when they heard the music they all bowed down.
Musicians stop and start a couple of times to see if the crowd keep up.
OFFICIAL 2: Excuse me, they didn't all bow down.
NARRATOR 2: Oh yes they did!
OFFICIAL 1 AND OFFICIAL 2: (*Together*) Oh no they didn't!
NARRATOR 2: Pardon?
OFFICIAL 1 AND OFFICIAL 2: (*Together*) Oh no they didn't!
NARRATOR 2: So who didn't?
OFFICIAL 1 AND OFFICIAL 2: (*Together*) They didn't! (*Pointing to Shadrach, Meshach and Abednego*)
NARRATOR 2: Well, what have we here? Three men from a foreign country disobeying our king. The officials were so pleased to find something about Shadrach, Meshach and Abednego to snitch on, that they ran to tell the king.

OFFICIAL 1 AND OFFICIAL 2: (*Running, and pushing each other to be first.*) Your Majesty! (*They bow down at Nebuchadnezzar's feet.*) Shadrach, Meshach and Abednego won't bow down and worship your statue.
NARRATOR 1: King Nebuchadnezzar was furious. So he sent for the three young men and said, 'I hear that you refuse to worship my gods and the gold statue I have set up. Now I am going to give you one more chance. If you bow down and worship the statue when you hear the music, everything will be all right. But if you don't, you will at once be thrown into a flaming furnace. No god can save you from me.' (Daniel 3:13-15 CEV).
SHADRACH, MESHACH, ABEDNEGO: Your Majesty, we don't need to defend ourselves. The God we worship can save us from you and your fiery furnace. But even if he doesn't, we still won't worship your gods and the gold statue you have set up.
NARRATOR 2: King Nebuchadnezzar was so angry that he had the men tied up and thrown into the furnace. (*Officials mime this action, or tie up the prisoners with toilet paper.*) Then the king looked into the furnace and was amazed by what he saw.
NEBUCHADNEZZAR: Hey! I thought I threw three men into that furnace; how come there are four? That other guy looks like a god! Get them out of there!
NARRATOR 2: The three came out. Everyone smelt them, looked at them and touched them (*suitable actions mimed*), but not one hair of their heads was even a tiny bit singed.
NEBUCHADNEZZAR: Praise the God of Shadrach, Meshach and Abednego! He is so great and powerful. Those three trusted him with their lives and look what he did for them. No one is to say anything against this God... or else!
NARRATOR 1: After this happened, the king appointed Shadrach, Meshach, and Abednego to even higher positions in Babylon Province (Daniel 3: 30 CEV).

Discussion starter:
Using the drama, discuss how and why Shadrach, Meshach and Abednego trusted God even when they were likely to die.

Nehemiah builds a wall

Bible base: Nehemiah 4; 6:15,16

The following is a story for the children to join in with mime as you tell it.

Divide the children into two groups to represent either Nehemiah and his friends or Sanballat and his followers and choose two leaders or two children who read well, to read out the following script. Nehemiah and his friends should mime everything said by the first narrator, while Sanballat and his followers should mime everything said by the second narrator. The narrators should pause, where marked, to enable their group to mime an appropriate action or to repeat a phrase.

Tip: It would be a good idea to send the two groups away for a brief practice before trying to put the whole thing together.

NARRATOR 1: The Emperor of Persia appointed Nehemiah as governor of Judah and allowed him to return to his former home in Jerusalem. Once Nehemiah had reached Jerusalem and inspected the ruined walls, he immediately set about organising the rebuilding. He divided the people into families (*pause*) and gave each family the task of rebuilding the section of wall nearest to their home. (*Pause*)

NARRATOR 2: When Sanballat heard that the Jewish people had begun to rebuild the walls of Jerusalem, he and his friends were very angry. Sanballat said, 'What do these miserable Jews think they are doing?' (*Pause*) And Tobiah, his friend, laughed and said, 'What kind of wall could they ever build? Even a fox could knock it down!' (*Pause*) Then Sanballat, Tobiah and all their friends gathered together to watch the Jewish people build the wall and to poke fun at them. (*Pause*) 'Huh! They'll never build a proper wall, it'll soon fall down!' (*Pause*)

NARRATOR 1: Nehemiah heard all the ridicule and mocking, and prayed that God would help him and give him strength (*pause*) and the Jewish people continued to build the wall. (*Pause*) Gates were added, and bolts and bars for locking the gates. (*Pause*) The people worked well and soon the wall was half its full height.

NARRATOR 2: This upset Sanballat and his followers even more. (*Pause*) The building made them feel nervous. They most probably wondered if Nehemiah was planning some kind of rebellion. Eventually, they came together to hatch a plot. (*Pause*) They decided to attack Jerusalem and create confusion.

NARRATOR 1: The Jewish people knew that their enemies wanted to harm them, so they prayed to God and asked for help. (*Pause*) Then they returned to building the wall, but they appointed half the men to stand guard, day and night. (*Pause*) Even those who were rebuilding the wall worked with one hand and kept a weapon in the other, and when they went to sleep at night they all kept their weapons close at hand. (*Pause*)

NARRATOR 2: Time after time, Sanballat and his followers plotted to attack the Jews. (*Pause*)

NARRATOR 1: But each time the Jews were on their guard, because some Jewish people living outside the city had come to warn them about the plans of their enemies. (*Pause*)

NARRATOR 2: Sanballat and his friends became more and more angry as the gaps were closed and the wall grew higher and higher. (*Pause*)

NARRATOR 1: Nehemiah's workforce was growing tired and some people didn't have enough money to buy food. (*Pause*) So Nehemiah invited them to eat at the governor's table. (*Pause*) Sometimes he fed up to one hundred and fifty people at his table. After just fifty-two days the whole wall was finished and the Jews stood back to admire their work. (*Pause*) They knew that they couldn't have finished this massive wall without God's help, and they thanked him for answering their prayers.

NARRATOR 2: Meanwhile, Sanballat and his unpleasant friends felt pretty stupid. (*Pause*) They had thought that the Jews would never finish the wall, but they had reckoned without God's help.

A job well done!

Bible base: Nehemiah 4; 6:15,16

Cast

NEHEMIAH and the **INTERVIEWER** (two adults or children who read well). The interviewer's lines could be read from a clipboard but, if possible, Nehemiah should learn or ad lib his lines. It would be best if the actors read through their lines beforehand.

Props: a clipboard (optional); a real or pretend microphone.

INTERVIEWER: Welcome to this special broadcast of *TV Jerusalem*. Today we have come to the walls of the city to join in the celebrations. As you will know, Jerusalem has been in ruins for many years since the Babylonians conquered our fine city, but now the walls have been completely rebuilt, thanks to the initiative of our special guest, Nehemiah. Well sir, this must be a very special day for you.

NEHEMIAH: It certainly is! It's a day when we can really thank God for all that he's done.

INTERVIEWER: Rebuilding the walls wasn't always easy, was it?

NEHEMIAH: No, far from it! When we started, the whole job seemed enormous. I remember going round the walls of the city at night, inspecting all the damage. I knew then that the job would be impossible on our own. However, with God's help, anything is possible.

INTERVIEWER: Apart from the size of the job, there were other problems, weren't there?

NEHEMIAH: Oh yes, there were people who didn't want us to rebuild the walls. They ridiculed and mocked us and even planned to attack us.

INTERVIEWER: So, how did you cope? Didn't you ever feel like giving up?

NEHEMIAH: Well, to be honest, I sometimes felt like it, but we always prayed when we especially needed help, and God always heard and answered our prayers. Today we are celebrating something which we could never have done on our own. God helped us to rebuild the walls in record time. It has taken just fifty-two days from start to finish. Today we are here to praise and thank God for helping us and protecting us.

INTERVIEWER: Thank you for talking to us. I can see that we'd better stop now as the celebrations are about to start.

At this point, move into a special time of praise and worship. If possible, bring in extra musicians and let the children join in with maracas and tambourines. If there are no musicians available, play a short, lively extract from a suitable praise tape.

Get ready for Jesus

Bible base: Luke 1:67–80; 3:1–18

In this version of Luke 1:67–80; 3:1–18, each time you say, 'Get ready!' the children reply, 'Get the road ready!' Introduce it with a reminder of the first part of Luke 1.

When John was born, everyone was amazed. They all asked, 'What is this child going to be?' Zechariah, John's father, filled with the Holy Spirit, said, 'Praise the Lord God! He has sent the one who will save his people, just as he promised.' Get ready!

Get the road ready!

'And John, my son, you will get God's people ready for him. You will tell them that they can have their sins forgiven and be saved. What love God is showing us! It's like the sun rising in the morning, driving the darkness away.' Get ready!

Get the road ready!

Living out in the desert, John grew up to be a man. Then God gave him a message for the people. He went to the area near the river Jordan, and called out: 'Turn away from your sins and be baptised, and God will forgive all you have done wrong.' Get ready!

Get the road ready!

Crowds came to hear John. But they didn't all want to be baptised. John was angry. 'Do you think you can escape God's punishment? If you want to, you must turn your backs on sin and do what God wants.' Get ready!

Get the road ready!

So the people asked, 'What do we have to do, then?' John said, 'Share your food, clothes and whatever you have, with those in need.' Get ready!

Get the road ready!

John told the tax collectors: 'Now, don't cheat the people by collecting more money than you are supposed to.' Get ready!

Get the road ready!

He told the soldiers: 'Don't accuse people of things they haven't done.' Get ready!

Get the road ready!

So people began to think: 'Maybe John is God's promised Messiah, who will save us.' But John said, 'Someone else is coming. He is so great, I am not good enough even to untie his sandals. You come to me to be baptised in water. He will baptise with the Holy Spirit and with fire.' Get ready!

Get the road ready!

In every way he could, John told people the good news and said: 'Get ready!'

Get the road ready!

Discussion starter:
Afterwards, ask the children to sum up how the people were to prepare for Jesus. Look together at the summary of John's message in Luke 3:3.

Words of hope

GERALDINE WITCHER

Bible base: Luke 1:26–45

You will need Bibles or copies of Luke 1:26–45 with different parts highlighted.

Choral speaking is an effective way to convey a Bible passage: look for an opportunity for your group to share their reading with others in the church, or at a Christmas event in which your church is involved. Beforehand, copy out the passage, dividing it into the parts of narrator, Mary, Gabriel and Elizabeth. With a younger group you may want to stop at verse 38. If your group is large enough, longer speeches can be broken down into two parts, eg Gabriel in verses 30–33. Aim to have at least three children in each group.

Introduce the passage by recalling the first part of Luke. Luke has introduced us to an old couple: now we meet a young woman, who was engaged to be married. Ask the children what kind of hopes they think she might have had.

Explain that the children themselves will be presenting the Bible story. Divide them into groups and give them a copy of the whole text with their part highlighted.

Read the passage aloud once yourself, with the children following their scripts. Now practise reading it out a few times, bringing children in at the right time. Once the children are fluent, start to put in dynamics, whispering some parts and shouting others.

Share your reading with others.

Use this technique to look at other Bible passages too.

What a surprise!

MAXINE RAWLINGS AND JEAN MITCHELL

Bible base: Matthew 1:18–25

This sketch is an interview with Joseph by an imaginary TV station. You may wish to create your own studio and name the TV station as you choose. There is scope in the script to allow for imaginative sound effects (SFX) should you wish.

Cast
TWO REPORTERS – Chris and Jules
JOSEPH

Props: things to suggest being in a TV studio: microphones, headphones, cardboard box TV cameras, etc.

CHRIS: Today on *What a Surprise!* we've come to surprise a man who's got a very big day tomorrow – he's getting married.

JULES: His name is Joseph, and we've come to his carpenter's shop to give him *What a Surprise! They knock on the door. SFX.*

JOSEPH: (*Opening the door*) Yes?

CHRIS AND JULES: *What a Surprise!*

JOSEPH: What?

CHRIS: We're from (*name of TV station*), and you're on camera.

JULES: And congratulations for the big day tomorrow. Are you looking forward to it?

JOSEPH: Thank you. Yes.

CHRIS: You must love Mary very much.

JOSEPH: Oh yes. She's very special.

JULES: Now tell us: do you think you will have a family soon?

JOSEPH: Oh yes, we're going to have a boy.

JULES: You sound very certain.

JOSEPH: Well, it's what the angel said.

CHRIS AND JULES: The angel! (*SFX: gasps.*)

JOSEPH: Yes, he came to me when I was asleep and said that Mary is going to have a boy. It's God's Holy Spirit who has made it possible. The child won't really be my son in the normal way.

CHRIS: And you're still going to marry her?

JOSEPH: To be honest, when I heard that she was pregnant I wasn't at all sure. But the angel explained it all. Did you know that King David was one of my ancestors?

CHRIS: And *you* will bring the baby up?

JOSEPH: Of course. He'll be our son. We're going to call him Jesus.

JULES: Ah! That's what my baby son is called too – after his grandfather.

JOSEPH: The angel said I should call him Jesus because of what the name means. Because he will save his people from their sins.

CHRIS: (*Amazed*) Save his people...

JULES: That's all we've got time for. Thank you, Joseph.

CHRIS: Save his people...

JULES: We've enjoyed talking to you.

CHRIS: Save...

(*Joseph closes the door. SFX*)

CHRIS AND JULES: (*Looking at each other*) What a surprise!

(*They walk off shaking their heads.*)

On the record

DAVID BELL

Bible base: Luke 2:1–7

Use the following script to retell Luke 2:1–7. Ideally, the part of Mary should be learned or improvised.

Cast
REPORTER
MARY

Props: script; clipboard; microphone; paper; pens.

REPORTER: Today in *On the Record* on (*name of TV station*) we have a special report on the census. I'm here in the historic town of Bethlehem, the birthplace of King David a thousand years ago. I'm standing outside the census office and I'm going to ask the people here what they think of the census. (*Waving to Mary who is standing around*) Excuse me, I'm from (*name of your TV station*). Could I talk to you?

MARY: Yes, I suppose so. I'm just waiting for my husband.

REPORTER: Can you tell me what you think of the census?

MARY: Well, I did think it was just a big nuisance having to travel all this way.

REPORTER: How far have you come?

MARY: Down from Nazareth. But it's so important for us to be here.

REPORTER: You think the census is important?

MARY: I know God wanted us to be here in Bethlehem, for the baby to be born.

REPORTER: You've just had a baby?

Congratulations! It must have been difficult being away from home.

MARY: Well, it hasn't been easy, but we've managed. It's amazing what you can do with warm hay and good baby clothes. What matters is that this is the right place for God's special king to be born.

REPORTER: God's special king?

MARY: Oh yes.

REPORTER: Are you saying that your baby is some special king?

MARY: Oh yes – like the angel said.

REPORTER: (*With a patronising smile*) Well, it's been good to hear your views...

MARY: That's what we've been told – God's special king.

REPORTER: ... but we must see who else we can talk to.

MARY: Ooh! There they are at last. (*Goes off calling*) Joseph!

REPORTER: (*Disbelieving*) A king lying in hay. Very sad! (*Going off the other way*) Excuse me, sir!

Discussion starter:
Ask each group to read Luke 2:5–7 and to think of a question which they would like to ask Mary about the circumstances of Jesus' birth. Comment on how little we know about Jesus' birth. The big surprise is that the special king, promised by God, was born into an ordinary family in poor surroundings.

Crossed lines

SHEILA HOPKINS

Bible base: Matthew 2:1–12

In this sketch, two television interviews have become mixed up. They should take place in separate studio areas. Each time the action switches from one to the other, the performers should remain still until they pick up the action again. The smoother the switches, the funnier the sketch will be. Make a strong contrast between the two interviews:

Interview 1 is a friendly chat with one of the wise men, in the style of breakfast TV.

Interview 2 is a pushy news interview with one of Herod's staff.

Cast
TWO TV INTERVIEWERS
A WISE MAN
ONE OF KING HEROD'S STAFF

Props: things to suggest being in a TV studio: microphones, headphones, cardboard box TV cameras, wires across the floor, etc.

INTERVIEWER 1: Good morning and welcome to (*name of TV station*). This morning we have a very special guest in the studio. He's one of the wise men who have been causing quite a stir in Jerusalem this last week. So we're hoping to find out just why he has travelled from the East on a...

INTERVIEWER 2: Hello! Welcome to *Good Morning Jerusalem* which comes live from Herod's...

INTERVIEWER 1: camel. Good morning to you, Mr Balthazar. May I start by asking you why you set out on this journey?

MR BALTHAZAR: I study the stars. One night a very special star appeared in the...

INTERVIEWER 2: palace. Rumours have been spreading all over Jerusalem during the night. They say that King Herod has seen the...

MR BALTHAZAR: sky. I have studied the stars for many years. I knew what this one must mean – it heralded the birth of...

INTERVIEWER 2: one of King Herod's attendants. Thank you for joining us. I gather that King Herod has been holding meetings with the most important people in the country – the chief priests and...

MR BALTHAZAR: a baby who is to be a new king of the Jews. So my friends and I decided to...

HEROD'S ATTENDANT: consult one of the chief priests and teachers of the law about the rumours of a new king being born. They were able to tell His Majesty that...

MR BALTHAZAR: it was certainly a long journey. We came here to Jerusalem hoping to...

HEROD'S ATTENDANT: find in the books of the prophets that the Messiah will be born in Bethlehem.

INTERVIEWER 2: We have the leaked document which says that King Herod secretly met with foreigners in the night. Apparently he wants them to find the child for him.

HEROD'S ATTENDANT: I'm afraid I can't possibly...

MR BALTHAZAR: worship him. That's why we have come all this way.

INTERVIEWER 1: We hope you'll come back to (*name of TV station*) and tell us what happens next in your story.

INTERVIEWER 2: No doubt it will run and run.

INTERVIEWER 1: In the meantime, this is Jake/Judy Josephs saying good...

INTERVIEWER 2: morning, live from the palace.

The big fight †

HUGH BOORMAN

Bible base: Luke 4:1–13

Cast

TWO BOXING COMMENTATORS – Dick and Harry.

Dick and Harry are seated at a desk with microphones, facing the audience, as if observing the boxing ring waiting for the fight to start.

DICK: Well, welcome to this heavyweight contest of the world. Harry, do you know much about tonight's two opponents?

HARRY: I certainly know about Satan, Dick. He's been around a long time and has got an incredible record. He's won every contest he's been in ... every one by knockout!

DICK: Every single one?

HARRY: Well, rumour has it that he lost his very first fight but he denies it.

DICK: And how about his opponent, Jesus?

HARRY: Now, he's a bit of an unknown quantity. Some say that he has been around longer than Satan but he's only just come to the public's notice.

DICK: So, who are you putting your money on to win this bout?

HARRY: Satan, naturally. He is such an expert at his work. I don't think that anyone can face him.

DICK: The fight is about to start. Perhaps, Harry, you can talk us through the match.

HARRY: Thanks, Dick. Well, here comes Satan straight into the attack. Oh, and just listen to that!

DICK: He's told Jesus to turn that stone into bread!

HARRY: Yes, Dick, that Satan doesn't pull any punches, does he? He goes straight in with a really powerful temptation. If Jesus wants to be anything, he's going to need the backing of the crowd and what better way of gaining popularity than giving them free food.

DICK: But what's Jesus saying now? He's quoting from scripture. He says that 'Man cannot live by bread alone.' Well, that's a new one.

HARRY: You're right there, Dick. I don't think Satan was ready for that one. Still, it won't bother him

much. He's got plenty of temptations where that one came from. Look, here comes another now. Oh, just listen to that! He's now going for our desire to be powerful. He's telling Jesus that he can have all the kingdoms in the world if he worships Satan. How will he cope with that?

DICK: He's gone for scripture again!

HARRY: Yes, Dick, and what a defence! Straight to the truth of the matter. 'Worship the Lord our God and serve only him!' I've never seen someone stand up to Satan like this.

DICK: Could Satan be facing his first defeat here, do you think, Harry?

HARRY: Oh no, Dick, that would be too much to expect from this newcomer. Mark my words, Satan will grind him down in the end. Look, here he comes again.

DICK: What's Satan going for this time?

HARRY: Oh, he's really pulled out all the stops this time. He's gone for the way we like to see miracles from God rather than living a steady life of faith. He's telling Jesus to jump from the top of the temple so that God's angels will save him. And he's even playing him at his own game - he's using the Scriptures. This one will have Jesus down on his knees.

DICK: No, Harry, Jesus is standing up to him once more and it looks like he's gone for his favourite riposte again. Yes, it's the Scriptures! 'Do not put the Lord your God to the test.' Wonderful! Absolutely wonderful! What's happening now? He's withdrawing! Satan is withdrawing!

HARRY: What a turn-up for the books! Satan is, indeed, leaving the ring. Jesus has won this fight.

DICK: Is that the end of the road for Satan, then, Harry? Will he go into retirement?

HARRY: I doubt it, Dick. If I know Satan, he will be demanding a re-match as soon as possible.

DICK: Well, thank you, Harry, for your commentary. That's all we have time for, folks. For a blow-by-blow report of tonight's fight, read Luke's Gospel, chapter 4, verses 1-13. Goodnight.

Follow the Leader †

ANDREW BALE

Bible base: Luke 5:1-8

Cast
JESUS
INTERVIEWER
FOUR CANDIDATES

One man, the interviewer, is seated at a desk; the others are waiting to be interviewed. They should each be dressed in character: Man 1 as a TV Gladiator or Hercules; Man 2 as a boffin; Man 3 in the latest fashion; Man 4 is very ordinary and sits, dejected, with his head in his hands.

JESUS: *(Enters.)* Hi there, folks – JC's the name.
Today I'm playing the appointing game.
I'm looking for disciples who can strut their stuff
Through times of persecution when the going gets tough.
Now I've paid my pound and I've placed my ad,
And I'm waitin' here to see what replies I've had.

MAN 1: I'd like to come and follow if you'll have me, Lord.
I've a spear and a shield and a curly sword.
I know you'll never find a better bodyguard.
I can be your minder 'cos I'm mega hard.
I've got boots with toes made of hardened steel,
You can tickle my tummy and I will not squeal.
When the multitudes are messing and you feel dead beat,
Watch me bless them, Lord, with my fists and feet.

JESUS: I'm gonna fight with love, not with sticks and stones.
I'm after broken people not broken bones.
I'm here to heal the sick and set the prisoner free.
Chuck your sword away if you want to follow me.
Man 1 looks down at his feet, disappointed.

MAN 2: If you're looking for disciples, then what about me?
I'm articulate and clever with a great CV.
I've been to university, I've got my gong.
With my lucid perspicacity you can't go wrong.
I'm fluent in Latin and in Turkish too,
With a smattering of Greek and, of course, Hebrew.

I'll do your thinking for you, if you'll let me stay,
Which'll leave you with a lot more time to pray.

JESUS: But the wisdom I'll be sharing will be God's, not man's,
And the word I'll be declaring is the Father's plans.
The only education that my people need
Is to hear the proclamation that they can be freed.
It's important to be clever, but the big surprise
Is that no one's really clever in the Father's eyes.
Lay aside your colleges, forget your schools,
The ones who follow me will be known as fools.
Man 2 looks down at his feet, disappointed.

MAN 3: If you'll let me come and follow, it'll be worthwhile.
I'm a trendy cool dude and I'm dripping with style,
I've got bangles, I've got beads, I've got diamond rings,
I've more money and possessions than a hundred kings.
I could buy you converts, I could buy you souls.
I could use my petty cash to meet your goals.
If you take me on, you'll be glad you did.
If you take me on, then I'll slip you fifty quid.

JESUS: Keep your money, son, you're no use to me.
Take your cash and stash and your false security,
Give it all away, go and treat the poor,
Give it all away 'til you're rich no more.
If you want to follow me, you can pack real quick,
Bring your hat and coat and a walking stick.
That's all you're gonna need if you join my fight,
The folk who follow me will be travelling light.
Man 3 looks down at his feet, disappointed.

JESUS: *(To Man 4)* Now what about you? Do you think
you could
Get up and follow me? 'Cos I think you should.
I'm looking for disciples who can strut their stuff
Through times of persecution when the going gets tough.
I'm on my way to heaven, but I'm going via hell.
The pay's not good, but the perks are swell.
So what do you say? Will you follow me, lad?

MAN 4: If you knew me, Lord, then you'd know I'm bad.
I'm a worker, not a leader, not the kind you need,
I'm a coward, Lord, I can barely read.
I'm poor and worthless, lowest of the low.
Thanks for the offer, but the answer's 'No!'

JESUS: You're the one I need! What a candidate!
What a man! What a find! Let's celebrate!

You're right, you're useless, with little self–worth,
You're the very reason that I came to earth.
When it comes to filling, then the Father pleads
For empty people, they're the sort he needs.
No talent, no money, no pretence, no show,
Just a heart that says 'Maybe', though the voice says 'No!'

6

Zebedee phones home

MARINA BROWN

Bible base: Matthew 4:18-25

This is a dramatic monologue in which Zebedee talks to his wife on the phone, relating the events of Matthew 4:18-25. Ask a leader or another church member to rehearse the script. If possible, it should be memorised. They will also need to prepare by reading the passage.

Cast
ZEBEDEE

Props: a telephone.

Zebedee is dressed as a fisherman. There is a telephone on stage. It rings and Zebedee answers it. It is his wife.

Hello. Galilee 4483. Zebedee and Sons. How can I ...? Oh, it's you, Golda. Where have you been? I've been trying to speak to you all afternoon, but there's been no reply... OK, OK, I know the market's busy on a Sunday, but just listen a moment, will you? I'm going to be late home... No! I haven't been to the inn, I've been fishing all day - on my own ... Well, something's happened to the boys, James and John. No, they're fine... Calm down a moment, will you?... There hasn't been an accident!... Listen Golda! PLEASE! James and John have gone away.

No, they haven't gone because of the way I row the boat: they've gone because Jesus asked them to... I know it's incredible... I know they don't usually do what they're told, but they have this time... I was there when it happened. Jesus was walking along the shore, with those two brothers, Simon and Andrew Whatsisname. We'd seen them fishing from the shore earlier on. They hadn't caught much, by the look of it. You know how Simon's always saying what a big catch of fish they've had... Yes, all right,

I'm coming to that...

Well, stop interrupting then! We had just got aboard the boat when the three of them came up to us - Jesus, Simon and Andrew. We were getting the nets ready. We were late, and I wanted to get going. Anyway, Jesus just called to the boys across the water. 'James, John!' he called. He's got a loud voice. You could hear him quite clearly. And then, before I had a chance to realise what was happening, James and John both jumped out of the boat and went to join Jesus...

What do you mean, didn't I try to stop them? I couldn't! It was too late! I heard Jesus talking to them as they waded ashore. He said something about them following him, and teaching them to catch men!... I know it sounds odd!... You know, Golda, all my life I've wanted to be in business with my sons: Zebedee and Sons. But they're not boys any more, are they, Golda? They're men. Fishermen. They're old enough to make up their own minds. Golda, there's something different about Jesus... No, I don't know him well, but somehow I can understand what our boys have done. It's exciting for them... I don't know, there's just something about Jesus that is worth following... Golda? *Zebedee hangs up the phone, shrugs and leaves the stage.*

Discussion starter:
After the performance, get the children to ask Zebedee questions about what has happened to him and his family, then look together at Matthew 4: 23-25. Work in small groups to prepare short messages which James and John might leave on Zebedee's answering machine to say what they are seeing and hearing as they travel with Jesus. Point out that following Jesus was exciting, but it also meant leaving things behind.

There's some wine in my bucket!

CLIVE DE SALIS  4

Bible base: John 2:1-12

Cast
THREE WAITERS – Eli, Jo and Sam
HEAD STEWARD

Props: up to six buckets; wine glass or beaker; two identical stone or china jugs, one containing blackcurrant squash for wine; plates; tea towels; trays; table; screen or staging to form a doorway (optional).

The play takes place in the kitchen during a wedding. Actors enter and exit the kitchen through a doorway at the rear of the stage area. Jo is busy in the kitchen.

ELI: (*Entering with Sam*) Hurry up with those plates.

JO: OK. (*Jo leaves with plates of food.*)

ELI: Did I hear that child ask for tomato ketchup on his wedding cake?

SAM: You did! No accounting for taste!

ELI: The customer is always right – that's what we say.

JO: (*Entering*) Are the glasses ready for the toast? The speeches are starting.

SAM: Where's the wine?

ELI: (*Holding up an empty jug, says loudly*) Oh, no! We've finished it! What are we going to do?

JO: (*Looking through the door*) That lady – Mary – she's signalling to me. I'll see what she wants. (*Jo leaves.*)

SAM: Where did all the wine go?

ELI: They drank loads before the meal and they've drunk the rest with the meal!

SAM: Do we serve water then?

ELI: We can't serve water – not to toast the bride and groom!

SAM: Well, what are we going to do?

ELI: I don't know! Let's think. (*Both strike thinking poses.*)

JO: (*Entering*) She says to do whatever Jesus says.

ELI: What are you talking about?

JO: Mary. She saw we were worried and asked what was going on.

ELI: (*Angry*) Oh great! We run out of wine and you tell the guests. I'd better talk to her. (*Eli leaves.*)

SAM: So, who's Jesus?

JO: The one who brought all his mates with him – he's Mary's son.

SAM: So, we're to do whatever Jesus says?

JO: That's right.

ELI: (*Entering*) He says to fill six cleaning bowls with water.

JO: WATER!

ELI: Yes, water.

SAM: But you don't toast the bride and groom with water. You said so yourself.

ELI: I know – but she said to do whatever he says and he says to fill them with water – all six of them!

JO: What a day! One family wants tomato sauce on everything and now one wants to toast the bride and groom in washing water!

SAM: We'd better go and do what he said. You go and find out what happens next!

(*Eli leaves. Sam and Jo take buckets to an imaginary pump and fill them.*)

JO: Maybe it's some strange Galilean custom?

SAM: Maybe it's just a joke.

ELI: (*Returning*) He says to take it to the steward in charge of the wedding...

JO AND SAM: (*Together and slowly*) Y... e... s.

ELI: ... and let him taste it.

JO AND SAM: NO!

ELI: YES!

JO AND SAM: NO!

SAM: No way!

ELI: Yes way!... We've got to!

SAM: You take it to the steward then!

ELI: I would but... but... but...

JO: But what?

ELI: But... but I'm busy. (*Jo and Sam look around to try and see what Eli is busy doing.*)

SAM: Busy?

ELI: Look! 'The customer is always right' is our motto – so let's do it! And, as head waiter, I say that you should do it, Jo!

JO: You're the head waiter. You do it!

ELI: Sam will go with you.

SAM: Not unless you come too!

ELI: OK. We'll all go! (*Turns to leave, then stops and turns suddenly.*) No – we'll bring the steward in here to taste it and that way the guests won't see him spitting out the washing water.

JO: Right! I'll get the steward. (*Jo leaves. Sam takes the jug containing the 'wine' and pretends to fill it from the bucket. Jo returns with the steward.*)

ELI: (*Nervously*) Er... we'd like you to try this. (*Sam pours a glass and is amazed by the colour of the 'water'. Hands it to the steward who drinks. Eli and Jo can't look, ready to blame someone else.*)

STEWARD: Nice! ⎫
ELI: It was Mary! ⎬ (*Simultaneously*)
JO: It was Jesus! ⎭

STEWARD: Very nice! (*Sam looks into jug. Eli and Jo together slowly turn and look down into the bucket.*)

JO: (*In disbelief*) ... from the cleaning bucket...?

STEWARD: What did you say?

JO: Nothing!

ELI: What a clean 'buckette' – you know – 'what a clean bouquet', as one might say!

STEWARD: Yes, it is a fine bouquet. It's strange, most people serve the best wine first, wait till the guests are happy and then serve the cheap stuff – but you kept the best wine to last. Why?

SAM: Well…

JO: Because…

ELI: Because... because everything that went before was preparing the way for this – the high point of the whole wedding – the celebration of the marriage!

STEWARD: Excellent! Well – what are you waiting for? Offer this wine to everyone and give it freely to anyone who asks!

JO: Yes, sir!

SAM: Right away!

Jo, Sam, Eli and the steward leave the kitchen carrying jugs or trays.

THERE'S SOME WINE IN MY BUCKET! CLIVE DE SALIS

The perfect prayer

NEIL PUGMIRE

Bible base: Luke 11:1-13

Cast

DR FREDERIC HUGEBRAIN
PROFESSOR HAROLD VON CLEVER–TROUSERS

If more children want to be involved, they can be the professor's helpers and can hand him chemicals at appropriate points. Ideally, they should all look identical, wearing white laboratory coats and glasses with thick lenses. If possible, the actors' hair should be gelled to stick up at the top and out at the sides – or wigs could be used.

Props: props to suggest the professor's laboratory, including a vat, bottles of horrible-looking chemicals labelled 'sorry', 'forgiveness', 'praise', 'please', etc and a computer screen; white laboratory coats and thick glasses for the actors.

Harold is mixing chemicals in the vat with a big wooden spoon. He has a manic expression on his face. Frederic enters and Harold has to stare at him closely through his glasses before he realises who it is.

HAROLD: (*who speaks with a pronounced accent*) Aha! Velcome to our world-famous laboratory, Dr Hugebrain! Vot is it zat ve can do for you?

FREDERIC: I have a special request from the churches, Professor Clever-Trousers. They want you to create the perfect prayer.

HAROLD: Ze perfect prayer! Ah – zis is very important! I haff somezinks here vich ve may be able to use. Vill you help me, Dr Hugebrain?

FREDERIC: I vill! Erm… I mean, I will!

HAROLD: Ze perfect prayer! (*He grabs 'sorry' bottle.*) Ve vill need to say sorry to God for ze zings ve do wrong. So zis is to ask him to forgive us. (*He pours it into the vat.*) And ve vill also need help to forgive ze others when zay do zings ve do not like. (*He pours in more of the same.*)

FREDERIC: What about this, Professor? (*Picking up the 'praise' bottle*) A bit of telling God how brilliant he is?

HAROLD: Ya, ya! Ve need lots of zat! (*Harold pours it in.*) And of zis – ze request for all ze good zings ve need every day! (*He pours from the 'please' bottle.*)

FREDERIC: (*Picks up another bottle.*) What about this one? (*Reads label.*) 'Asking God for a new girlfriend'? (*He goes to pour it in.*)

HAROLD: (*Snatches it out of Harold's hand.*) Erm, no… zat is a special one I am working on for myself… erm, I mean for my friend! (*Picks up another bottle.*) Ve have zis one vich helps us to call God 'Dad' because he is like a father to us.

FREDERIC: And this one asks for help to keep away from situations that will make us do the wrong thing. (*He pours it in.*)

HAROLD: OK! Now I haff connected sensors from ze computer to my mixture of chemicals. It should now give us a read-out of Ze Perfect Prayer! (*He presses some buttons.*)

FREDERIC: (*Reading what comes up on the screen*) It says: 'Dear Dad, you are fantastic and we can't wait for things to be perfect on earth like they are in heaven. Please give us the food we need each day. Please forgive us when we do things wrong, and help us to forgive others too. Please help us keep away from temptation. Amen.'

HAROLD: Aha! I zink I've heard somezink like that before – but I can't remember vere… (*They gaze at the screen, frowning.*)

Two a penny

LUCY MOORE  6

Bible base: Matthew 10:29-31

Cast
TRADER
FIVE SPARROWS

Props: Five strong wooden blocks.

The scene is a market stall. The sparrows should be 'perched' in a row on their blocks.

TRADER: Roll up! Roll up! Buy your wonderful fresh sparrows here! Nice, plump sparrows. Priceless! Roll up! Roll up!

SPARROW 1: Hear that? 'Wonderful' he called us! Isn't that great!

SPARROW 2: Well, we are wonderful!

SPARROW 3: Yeah, I mean, cast your beady eyes over me - have you ever seen a smarter sparrow in your life?

SPARROW 4: You can talk all you want about birds of paradise, peacocks and all that, but you just can't beat a sparrow. Priceless, he called us! Priceless!

SPARROW 5: Um... excuse me, but...

SPARROW 1: Wonderful - we certainly are. Look at us all. Beautiful brown feathers...

SPARROWS 2,3,4: Yeah, brown feathers...

SPARROW 1: Little pointy beaks...

SPARROWS 2,3,4: (*Echoing*) Little pointy beaks...

SPARROW 1: Dinky little feet...

SPARROWS 2,3,4: Oh so dinky...

SPARROW 1: And a tweet to end all tweets!

SPARROW 5: Excuse me...

SPARROW 1: Give 'em the tweet, boys.

SPARROWS 1,2,3,4: Tweet, tweet, tweet.

TRADER: Very fresh sparrows here, lots of meat on 'em. Make a lovely stew, Madam - or why not kebab them? Sparrow sausage - now there's a delicacy.

SPARROW 1,2,3,4: Tweet, tweet, tweet.

SPARROW 1: We are priceless!

SPARROW 2: Worth a king's ransom!

SPARROW 3: No wonder people want to buy us!

SPARROW 5: (*Interrupting*) Excuse me! Do you realise what we're being sold for?

SPARROW 4: We'll be rich ladies' pets, in golden cages. Bird baths with built-in jacuzzis, luxury bird seed...

SPARROW 5: (*Loudly*) No! (*Continues quietly when he has everyone's attention*) They want to EAT us. We're even cheaper than chicken.

SPARROW 1: What? Surely not!

TRADER: Only two pence for the four of them. Tell you what, Madam, as it's you, I'll throw in one for free. Five sparrows for two pence - what a bargain.

SPARROW 2: We're only worth two pence? Oh no. The shame. (*Sobs*)

SPARROW 5: Cheer up. It depends on your point of view.

SPARROW 3: What do you mean?

SPARROW 5: These people think we're only worth two pence. But when I was perched on the window-ledge of a house yesterday, I heard this bloke in sandals say that God doesn't forget a single one of us. We're worth more than two pence to him.

SPARROW 4: That's a fat lot of good when we're turned into sparrow stroganoff.

SPARROW 5: But don't you see? It's God's view of us that matters, not these people's.

SPARROW 1: I just wish there were some people around who felt the same as he does. I mean how much do you think *they're* worth for heaven's sake?

SPARROW 5: As much as anyone's willing to pay, I suppose.

TRADER: Roll up! Get your sparrows here! Priceless bargain! Roll up!

39

Shocking!

NICK HARDING

Bible base: Matthew 18:1-5; 19:13-15

In this sketch, two disciples are discussing the events of Matthew 19:13-15. You may find it better to improvise your own words rather than learning the script, but make sure the surprise at what Jesus did, comes across.

Cast
DISCIPLE A
DISCIPLE B

A: I just don't understand it.
B: No, nor do I – I just don't understand it.
A: I'm shocked!
B: So am I!
A: I know he has strange ideas – that's why I follow him. But that incident back there with the children, well...
B: Yes, you'd have thought he would have been grateful. He's been so tired these last few weeks, and those crowds have followed us everywhere. I thought Jesus would be really pleased to have a rest and a sit-down, not angry with us because we tried to help him.
A: He just doesn't know how a respected teacher should behave, if you ask me! He'll talk to anyone: men, women, foreigners, even those kids! He doesn't seem to care whether they're important people or the lowest of the low.

B: I didn't think that Jesus would be bothered with a few children. It was so rude of those people to bring them along and expect him to be interested!
A: And then Jesus went and told us off in front of everyone. Us! As if we were doing something wrong. And all for the sake of a few children.
B: When I was little, I wasn't allowed anywhere near Rabbi Matthias. Except once a year we were taken for him to pray for us.
A: Jesus keeps amazing me. He even seems pleased to see babies! It's as if they're as important as adults to him. I just don't understand it!
B: No, nor do I – I just don't understand it!
(The two walk off saying, 'I just don't understand it!')

Discussion starter:
After the drama, read the Bible passage together. Reinforce the point that what Jesus did was very surprising in the culture of the time. He welcomed people who were seen as unimportant, such as young children. Ask the children to suggest other groups of 'unimportant' people who Jesus welcomed. They might be able to think of some specific examples from the Gospels.

Sheep tales*

MARY GREEN

Bible base: Matthew 18:10-14

Cast

ARAN AND AMOS (leaders, adults, older children who are familiar with script)
HELPER(S) to carry signs.

Props: signs saying '100 baaas later', 'On the other side of the hill', ' Important sheep, *very* important sheep'.

Set the scene for the children by saying that Jesus' disciples were asking him about who the greatest would be. Jesus brings on... a child! He continued to teach the disciples (adults) about children. Read Matthew 18:10-14. Say that Jesus asked a question: what would you do if you lost something that was important?

Introduce your sheep and shepherd. Explain that when the word 'sheep' is used in the drama, the children call out 'woolly sheep, *very* woolly sheep'. Point out to the children that this phrase is slightly different at the end of the story. There will be a special sign for them to read, which has the new phrase on. Practise together, then present the drama.

ARAN: Baa. I'm Aran. See that **sheep** with the wool on? That's my mum. And that one over there? He's not a **sheep** - he's our shepherd.

AMOS: … ninety-seven, ninety-eight...
ARAN: He smells like a **sheep** though; he spends so much time with us. He looks after us. See that dead lion lying over there: Amos did that.
AMOS: … ninety-nine, a hundred: he didn't get any of them.
ARAN: People say that **sheep** can only follow. If *you* had to walk up the hills round here, *you'd* follow someone who knew where he was going! *(Chews.)* People say that **sheep** all look alike. Amos doesn't say that. He knows every one of us.
AMOS: (*Could use names from the group, or...*) Dippy, Spot, Aran - one hundred **sheep**!
ARAN: (*Puffing*) Nearly got left behind... now where was I? Come to think of it, where am I? Help! Baaaaa! (*Wanders to corner of room. Helper walks across with sign saying '100 baaas later'.*)
ARAN: (*Faintly*) Baaa. (*Helper walks across with sign saying 'On the other side of the hill'.*)
AMOS: … ninety-eight, ninety-nine... (*Looks puzzled and mimes counting*) Ninety-eight, ninety-nine... I'm coming Aran! (*He rushes across the room.*)
ARAN: (*Barely audible*) Baa. (*Amos stops and changes direction towards sound. Leap of joy or loud 'Yes' as he sees Aran.*)
AMOS: (*Counting*) One (*pause*) very important **sheep**. (*Holds up sign for children to repeat 'important sheep, very important sheep'.*)

Sidney Spender, Super Spender

JUDITH MERRELL

Bible base: Matthew 18:21-35

Cast
BANK MANAGER
SIDNEY SPENDER
SHORTY

Props: desk and chair.

Inside a local bank.

MANAGER: Next! (*Enter Sidney. The Manager is seated at his desk.*)

SIDNEY: Spender, sir, Sidney Spender. Account number 489574.

MANAGER: Spender, ah yes! I have your file here. Now then, Mr Spender, you owe the bank £575,000. How do you propose paying back the money that you owe?

SIDNEY: £575,000… as much as that? I mean, I knew I owed the bank some money, but £575,000… it's staggering!

MANAGER: Exactly, Mr Spender.

SIDNEY: Well… I… err… suppose I could get a Saturday job and perhaps a paper round.

MANAGER: Mr Spender, we're talking about £575,000, not £75.

SIDNEY: Hmm! Yes, I see. Sounds rather serious, doesn't it?

MANAGER: Exactly, Mr Spender.

SIDNEY: It sounds like rather a lot of money, doesn't it?

MANAGER: Exactly, Mr Spender. How much is your house worth?

SIDNEY: About £120,000.

MANAGER: Your car?

SIDNEY: About £5,000.

MANAGER: That reduces your debt to £450,000.

SIDNEY: But I can't sell my house. Where would I live? And I can't sell my car. How would I get to work? And what about my family? What would they do?

MANAGER: You should have thought of that a little sooner, Mr Spender.

SIDNEY: I suppose I could sell the wife's car. We could just about manage without that.

MANAGER: (*Standing up*) Mr Spender, even if you sell your wife and the car, you still won't be able to pay back the £575,000 you owe us.

SIDNEY: Sell my wife!

MANAGER: Just a little joke, Mr Spender.

SIDNEY: Oh, I see.

MANAGER: No, I don't think you do see. You owe the bank £575,000. Even if you sell your house, your car, your TV, your video, your washing machine, your dishwasher, the furniture, the fixtures and fittings, the cutlery, the crockery and the canary, you still would not be able to pay back the £575,000 you owe us. As a result, Mr Spender, I'm going to have to declare you bankrupt and I'm afraid you'll have to go to prison.

SIDNEY: P… prison! Not prison! Please don't send me to prison. I'll do anything. I'll work day and night. My whole family will work day and night. I'll even sell my house and my car and the canary. Oh, please be patient. Just give me a little more time and I'll pay back all the money I owe you, but please don't send me to prison.

MANAGER: Hmm!

SIDNEY: Please! (*Falling to his knees*)

MANAGER: Well… err…

SIDNEY: Sir? (*Clutching the manager's knees*)

MANAGER: Well… I…

SIDNEY: Your Very Important Personness. (*Kissing his feet*)

MANAGER: Well… OK.

SIDNEY: OK?

MANAGER: I forgive you all the money that you owe. I'll let you off.

SIDNEY: I'm forgiven… I'm let off! Thank you. Thank you. (*Stands up, grabs the manager and hugs him rather too tightly.*)

MANAGER: (*With hardly any breath left*) That's quite all right. (*Aside to audience*) No point being a filthy rich bank manager if you can't spread a little happiness around! Off you go and tell the family the good news. (*Exit Bank Manager.*)

SIDNEY: (*Mimes leaving the bank and walking along the road outside.*) I'm forgiven. I'm free. I don't owe anyone any money. (*Enter Shorty.*) Shorty, my old friend, how are you?

SHORTY: Err… fine.

SIDNEY: Lovely day, isn't it? (*Manager enters and*

stands at the side watching)

SHORTY: Err… yes.

SIDNEY: Wonderful weather!

SHORTY: Err… wonderful.

SIDNEY: Now then, Shorty, you owe me some money. £75 to be exact. When are you going to give it to me?

SHORTY: Well, I could give you £5 today.

SIDNEY: Only £5. That's not enough.

SHORTY: And another £5 next week.

SIDNEY: What! How dare you? I want all the money today.

SHORTY: The whole £75?

SIDNEY: The whole £75. Today!

SHORTY: But I don't have £75. I can't give it to you.

SIDNEY: Do you know what happens to people who don't pay their debts?

SHORTY: Please, Sidney…

SIDNEY: They get thrown into prison. You're coming with me.

SHORTY: Oh, please be patient. Just give me a little time and I'll pay back all the money I owe you, but please don't send me to prison.

SIDNEY: It's too late for tears now. You're coming with me. *(Sidney drags him off by the scruff of the neck.)*

MANAGER: Wait a minute! Wait a minute, you worthless, ungrateful wretch! I saw everything. Don't you remember how much I forgave you?

SIDNEY: Yes, sir… Thank you, sir.

MANAGER: But you couldn't even forgive this man the measly £75 he owed you?

SIDNEY: Well… I… err…

MANAGER: Since you didn't let this man off the £75 he owed you, I will no longer let you off the £575,000 you owe me. You deserve a long holiday… in prison.

Exit Shorty and Manager, dragging Sidney by the scruff of his neck.

Wait till I tell you!*

FIONA WALTON  2

Bible base: John 12:12–16; Zechariah 9:9

Cast

MUM AND JOSH (This can be adapted to make either character male or female and it is best if they have prepared beforehand, although if necessary, they can read from copies of the script.)

Props: a coat with hoofprints on the back (black paper, tacked on). You could also use a washing-up bowl and a tea towel as props.

Josh arrives home, excited, wearing the coat. His mum is washing up.

MUM: Hello, dear. You've been out a long time.

JOSH: Mum, you'll never...

MUM: *(Not listening)* I expect you've been out with Reuben.

JOSH: Yes, but I've...

MUM: I hope you've not got up to any mischief, dear. You know what your Dad said last time.

JOSH: *(Exasperated)* I'm trying to tell you...

MUM: I've had such a busy day, no time to sit around like you do.

JOSH: I haven't been sitting...

MUM: Pass me the tea towel, Josh. *(Josh turns round so that the audience and Mum can see hoofmarks on the back of his coat. Mum gasps and then seems angry.)*

MUM: Joshua, where have you been? What have you been up to? Are you all right? Did you get trampled by old Mr Levi's mad mule? You must be more careful. Oh Josh!

JOSH: *(Loudly)* Mum! I've been trying to tell you! *(More gently)* I was playing with Reuben over by the city gate, and there were crowds of people.

MUM: Well, it is Passover, dear. There are always lots of people here for the holiday.

JOSH: Everyone was pushing and shoving, and we nearly got squashed against the city walls. They were all really excited. Then someone shouted, 'Here he is!', and everyone cheered. I couldn't see a thing, so this man gave me a leg-up and I saw Jesus, the teacher, riding Levi's smallest donkey.

MUM: But no one's ever ridden it!

JOSH: I know, but you'd never have guessed. It was so peaceful. Then everyone began tearing branches from the trees and waving them. Someone shouted, 'Praise God! Hosanna! God bless the King of Israel!' and we all joined in! It was wonderful!

MUM: *(Hugging him)* Oh no! Did the donkey go wild and trample all over you?

JOSH: No! The people round me were putting their coats on the ground for Jesus to ride over. I just had to give him mine. You'd have understood if you'd been there, Mum. *(Mum nods and looks moved.)* I just know he's special, Mum. They were calling him a king.

MUM: But he was only on a donkey.

JOSH: I don't think he's an ordinary king.

MUM: *(Thoughtfully)* But the King nevertheless... Don't you remember from school? The prophet Zechariah said, 'Everyone in Jerusalem, celebrate and shout! Your king … is coming to you. He is humble and rides on a donkey.' Josh, you've seen something very special today. *(Pause)* Give me your coat and I'll wash it for you.

Discussion starter:

If you're doing this sketch prior to Easter, you could follow it by saying that most people in Jerusalem did not like the idea that Jesus was God's special king, so they put him on trial before the governor, Pilate. What happened next was very sad. Read out John 19:12–22. Finish by saying, 'But that was not the end of the story, or the end of Jesus. He really is the King, and at Easter we'll be celebrating what happened.' You could ask the children, working in pairs, to make up a conversation between Josh and his mum that Friday evening.

Malchus' miracle

JUDITH MERRELL  4

Bible base: Matthew 26:47–56

Cast

COOKIE and **DEMAS**: two older and experienced slaves

MALCHUS and **CRESTUS**: two younger slaves, both lively and noisy

Props: kitchen equipment arranged on a table; two or three chairs.

The scene is the kitchen in the slaves' quarters of the High Priest's villa. Cookie and Demas are busy preparing a late supper.

COOKIE: *(Shouting)* Malchus! Crestus! Bother those boys! They're never around when there's work to be done.

DEMAS: Let me go and have a look. Perhaps I can find them. *(He gets up to go, but bumps into Malchus and Crestus who enter, very excited.)* Oof! Slow down, boys! Take care!

MALCHUS: *(Both speaking together)* You'll never guess what's happened!

CRESTUS: It was incredible!

COOKIE: Calm down, calm down! Now, where have you been? We've been calling you for over an hour.

MALCHUS: To Gethsemane.

CRESTUS: To the garden in Gethsemane.

DEMAS: *(Annoyed)* As if there isn't enough work for you to do here!

MALCHUS: But it was the master's idea.

CRESTUS: He wanted to drum up a crowd and he particularly asked for us.

COOKIE: For you two… the least experienced of all his slaves? I can't imagine why!

MALCHUS: He said it was because we're the noisiest of all his slaves.

DEMAS: Well, he's right about that!

MALCHUS: *(Grabbing a wooden spoon to demonstrate)* He gave me a torch to carry.

CRESTUS: *(Holding a rolling pin and fork)* And a club, and a burning torch to hold.

MALCHUS: And we had to march like this. *(They demonstrate.)*

CRESTUS: And he told us to look menacing… like this. *(They demonstrate.)*

COOKIE: *(Laughing but rescuing the cutlery from them)* So what happened next?

MALCHUS: Judas Iscariot, the man who was leading us at the front…

CRESTUS: He took us to the garden in Gethsemane.

MALCHUS: When we got there he told us that we'd come to arrest a man called Jesus.

CRESTUS: Jesus of Nazareth.

DEMAS: *(Puzzled)* Isn't that the man who does all those miracles?

CRESTUS: Exactly! Just wait until you hear what happened next!

MALCHUS: Judas said we had to keep close to him. The plan was that he'd walk up to Jesus and kiss him on the cheek, so we'd know who to arrest.

CRESTUS: I was expecting all kinds of trouble. After all, there were so many of us and we all had swords or clubs.

MALCHUS: But when we reached the middle of the garden, there was Jesus with a handful of his followers, and hardly any of them were armed. It was as if Jesus expected to be arrested.

CRESTUS: Anyway, that was when the miracle happened.

COOKIE: What miracle?

CRESTUS: Peter, one of Jesus' followers, went really wild! *(Picking up a wooden spatula and waving it threateningly)* He rushed at Malchus, waving his sword like a mad man.

MALCHUS: I tried to get out of his way, but it was too late! He chopped my ear right off!

COOKIE: What are you talking about? You've still got two ears, as plain as anything, one on each side of your head.

DEMAS: *(Examining Malchus' ear at close quarters)* Looks all right to me!

MALCHUS: Yes! But that's because of Jesus!

CRESTUS: There was blood everywhere! Really messy, it was. Yuk!

MALCHUS: *(Rubbing the ear)* And it hurt something terrible too.

CRESTUS: But Jesus walked right up to Malchus, reached out his hand and healed his ear, just like that!

MALCHUS: And he told Peter to put his sword

away. 'Anyone who lives by fighting will die by fighting', he said.

CRESTUS: He said that if he wanted to, he could call on his Father and ask him to send twelve armies of angels to rescue him, but he had been arrested so that the scriptures could be fulfilled.

MALCHUS: Then all his followers just ran away and left him. Jesus let himself be taken prisoner.

DEMAS: *(Shaking his head)* I don't know whether to believe you or not. It all sounds quite incredible.

COOKIE: I think we have to believe them, Demas. Even these two could not make up a story like this!

MALCHUS: *(Defiant)* There were lots of people with us. You've only got to ask them.

COOKIE: How does your ear feel now?

MALCHUS: Brilliant! Better than ever. That Jesus must be really special. I intend to find out more about him.

CRESTUS: Me too!

DEMAS: *(Scratching his head)* But there's something I still don't understand. If Jesus is so special, and if he performed so many miracles and that, why did they want to arrest him?

MALCHUS: *(Lowering his voice and looking around to see if anyone is listening in)* I don't know, but I think our master is involved in some kind of plot! I don't like it, I don't like it at all.

COOKIE: It sounds to me as if we should all try to find out more about Jesus. I reckon his arrest was a real put-up job!

What a scoop!

MARINA BROWN  **3**

Bible base: Matthew 28:1–10

Use the following sketch to introduce the events covered in Matthew 28:1–10. If three leaders are performing the sketch, encourage them to learn or improvise the lines rather than read straight from the script.

Cast
REPORTER
MARY 1
MARY 2

REPORTER: Good morning, viewers. I'm standing just outside the city of Jerusalem, which was shaken by a sudden and violent earthquake early this morning. This follows a whole series of strange events which many people are linking to the death, by crucifixion, of Jesus of Nazareth. Three days ago, at noon, the whole countryside was covered with darkness for three hours and an earthquake shook the city, splitting rocks apart, shaking open graves and ripping the special curtain in the temple from top to bottom. Fortunately, no one was hurt in the incident, but many people were treated for shock. Though most people were in bed for this latest earthquake, I've come onto the streets to get a few impressions from some early risers. *(Enter the two Marys.)* Good morning, ladies. Can you spare a moment to give us your impressions of this latest earthquake?

MARY 1: Earthquake? Oh, I'd forgotten about that. So much has happened since then. Besides, the angel…

REPORTER: Angel?

MARY 2: Yes, the angel saw that we were scared and he told us not to be afraid. Now, we really must get on.

REPORTER: Ladies, you've lost me! Who's this angel that you're talking about? Where did you see him?

MARY 1: The angel was sitting on a rock beside the tomb.

REPORTER: What tomb?

MARY 1: Jesus' tomb! We got up early this morning to go and visit his tomb.

MARY 2: We wanted to anoint his body with spices.

MARY 1: We'd been wondering who we could ask to help us roll away the huge stone at the entrance.

MARY 2: And we'd decided to ask the soldiers who were guarding the tomb, to help us.

MARY 1: In fact, we didn't need to worry about the stone, and the soldiers would have been useless anyway…

MARY 2: They were all in a dead faint – or maybe they'd been struck dumb with fright.

MARY 1: Grown men… I ask you! And all because of an earthquake and an angel.

REPORTER: The angel again…

MARY 2: He was a very nice angel, just sitting quietly on the stone by the open tomb. Mind you, he gave us a bit of a fright at first, with his dazzling appearance and his shining clothes.

MARY 1: But he soon put us right and he's given us such great news to pass on to the others.

REPORTER: *(Bewildered)* Others? More angels?

MARY 2: No, the disciples! We need to tell them to go to Galilee to meet Jesus.

REPORTER: But ladies, this earthquake has obviously unbalanced you! Jesus is dead. He was crucified two days ago. Don't you remember?

MARY 1: We thought he was dead, but he's not. He told us that he'd come back to life, and he has!

MARY 2: Yes, we've seen him, heard him, and even touched him!

REPORTER: You've actually seen him and heard him and touched him? This is amazing! Where is he? I've got to talk to him for myself. Tell me more…

MARY 1: There's no time now; we have to go and tell the others what we've seen. Why don't you go to Galilee? That's where Jesus said he was going. *(Exit the two Marys.)*

REPORTER: *(Puzzled)* Jesus is alive? *(More certain)* Jesus is alive! *(Joyfully)* Jesus is alive! Who cares about an earthquake? This is a world exclusive!

Gumpole of the Bailey

CLIVE DE SALIS

Bible base: Matthew 27:62-66; 28:11-15

Cast
PETER
JUDGE
TWO SOLDIERS – Marcus and Julius
GUMPOLE: defence barrister
KAVIAR: prosecuting barrister
JURY of up to twelve children

Props: a large card with the word 'GASP!' written on it.

Whenever a witness is called, each juror repeats the call, until the last juror who returns a question all the way back along the jurors to the judge. When you hold up the card, judge, jury and audience should gasp in amazement.

JUDGE: SILENCE in court. Are you Peter the disciple?
PETER: Yes, my Lord.
JUDGE: You are charged with having stolen the body of Jesus of Nazareth from his tomb, during Saturday night. Do you plead guilty or not guilty?
PETER: Not guilty, my Lord.
JUDGE: Kaviar, you may now present the case for the prosecution.
KAVIAR: Thank you, my Lord. We summon the first witness: the soldier.
JUDGE: Call the soldier!
JUROR 1: Call the soldier! *(And so on down the line of jurors)*
LAST JUROR: Which soldier? *(Back up the line of jurors to judge)*
JUDGE: *(To Kaviar)* Which soldier?
KAVIAR: Private Marcus, my Lord.
JUDGE: Call Private Marcus!
JUROR: Call Private Marcus! *(etc)*
LAST JUROR: Private Marcus, please come in. *(Marcus takes his place.)*
KAVIAR: Private Marcus, is it true that on Saturday night you were one of the guards at the tomb?
MARCUS: Yes, sir.
KAVIAR: Please tell the court, in your own words, what happened.
MARCUS: After the body had been put in the tomb,

we rolled the stone over the entrance. Then two of us were ordered to stay behind and guard it.
KAVIAR: So trouble was expected?
GUMPOLE: Objection! The prosecution is putting ideas into the witness's mind!
JUDGE: Overruled, Gumpole. You'll get your turn as defence lawyer later.
KAVIAR: Continue, Private.
MARCUS: So we stayed behind. About four in the morning, a man came, rolled away the big rock and stole the body.
KAVIAR: Is that it?
MARCUS: Umm, yes.
KAVIAR: Why didn't you stop him?
MARCUS: I was asleep at the time!
Hold up the 'GASP!' sign.
KAVIAR: Can you identify him?
MARCUS: Yes, sir! *(Pointing at Peter)* It was HIM! *(GASP!)*
PETER: It wasn't! I didn't!
JUDGE: SILENCE in the court!
KAVIAR: No more questions, my Lord.
JUDGE: Your witness, Gumpole.
GUMPOLE: Private, how many soldiers rolled the stone over the tomb?
MARCUS: Four. It was a big stone.
GUMPOLE: It was a big stone. A very big stone to need four soldiers to seal the tomb, but you said only one man, my client, rolled back the stone.
MARCUS: Well, he might be strong! *(GASP!)* No! *(Marcus suddenly has an idea)* It rolled downhill.
GUMPOLE: It rolled towards you?
MARCUS: Yes, I jumped out of the way!
GUMPOLE: I thought you said you were asleep! I put it to you that you weren't asleep and that it needed a whole gang to move the rock.
MARCUS: Or an angel. *(GASP!)*
GUMPOLE: Angel? You said an angel! Just one angel?
MARCUS: Umm, one, I think!
GUMPOLE: One angel! You think! You didn't see my client at all, did you?
MARCUS: I did, I did! Well, I think it was him!
GUMPOLE: Think it was him? With or without an angel? *(GASP!)* No further questions, my Lord.
JUDGE: You may step down. Call your next witness:

the soldier.

JUDGE: Call the soldier!

JUROR 1: Call the soldier! *(etc)*

LAST JUROR: Which soldier? *(etc)*

JUDGE: *(To Kaviar)* Which soldier?

KAVIAR: Private Julius, my Lord.

JUDGE: Call Private Julius!

JUROR 1: Call Private Julius! *(etc)*

LAST JUROR: Private Julius, please enter. *(Julius takes his place.)*

KAVIAR: Private Julius. On Saturday night, were you guarding the tomb?

JULIUS: Yes, sir.

KAVIAR: Tell the court, in your own words, what happened.

JULIUS: After the body had been put in the tomb, we rolled the stone over the entrance. Then two of us were ordered to stay behind and guard it.

GUMPOLE: So you guarded the tomb.

JULIUS: Yes, we did. At about four in the morning, a man came, rolled away the big rock and stole the body.

KAVIAR: Is that it?

JULIUS: Umm, yes.

KAVIAR: Didn't you stop him?

JULIUS: I was asleep at the time! *(GASP!)*

KAVIAR: Can you identify him?

JULIUS: Yes, sir. *(Pointing at Peter)* It was HIM!

PETER: It wasn't! *(GASP!)*

JUDGE: SILENCE in court!

KAVIAR: No further questions.

JUDGE: Your witness, Gumpole.

GUMPOLE: You said you were asleep. How then could you see anyone?

JULIUS: Umm. Well... Umm...

GUMPOLE: Can't explain, can you? Didn't the noise of the angel moving the rock wake you up? Weren't you frightened?

JULIUS: Of course I was frightened. I'd never seen an angel before!

GUMPOLE: An angel – so there *was* an angel there too. (*GASP!*) And did the angel take the body?

JULIUS: Oh no! The body walked out by himself!

GUMPOLE: So the body walked out. No further questions, my Lord.

JUDGE: WHAT? He says the body walked out – and you say, 'No further questions'! How can a dead body just walk out?

GUMPOLE: Well he must have come back to life again. Anyway, the point is that there is no evidence that Peter stole Jesus' body.

JUDGE: So Jesus rose from the dead?

GUMPOLE: That, my Lord, is not for this court to decide. The fact that Jesus is now alive is another story.

JUDGE: Very well, I find Peter the disciple NOT GUILTY. But it seems to me that if Jesus walked out of his own tomb, then that's a far more interesting case to discuss.

Rockety Rock

HELEN FRANKLIN AND THE ABERSOCH MISSION TEAM
ADAPTED BY DAVID BELL

Bible base: John 18:15-18,25-27; 21:15-25

Cast
NARRATOR

PETER

CHORUS (at least four people, ideally six or more)

The narrator tells the story of Peter's denial and restored relationship with Jesus in verse form. The chorus provide the following quiet background chant which remains the same throughout the sketch:

Rock Rock Rockety Rock: Rock Rock Rockety Rock;
<u>Rock Rock Rockety Rock</u>: Rock Rock Rockety Rock;
<u>Rock Rock Rockety Rock:</u> Rock Rock Rockety Rock;
<u>Rock Rock Rockety Rock</u>: <u>Rock Rock Rockety Rock;</u>
The Rock.

The narrator reads the four lines of the verse over the places which are underlined. Narrator and chorus all say 'The Rock' together. The chorus then silently count '2,3,4' before beginning the chant again.

The action is stylised and simple – most is slick movement between the verses with the actors then remaining still, but you may want to add occasional gestures or actions during the verses.

Chorus stand in a semicircle facing the audience. Peter stands facing them with his back to the audience.

Peter the Rock was Jesus' friend,
Ready to stick with him right to the end.
Jesus had said, 'Be strong; be firm!'
And Peter thought he would never turn.
The Rock.

(Peter turns to face the audience, crouches and warms hands at an imaginary fire.)

They came and arrested Jesus one night.
And Peter the Rock kept his master in sight.
A fire had been lit; people gathered about.
Peter went near so he wouldn't stand out.
The Rock.

(One of the chorus steps forward as a servant girl and points her finger at Peter. Peter shakes his head.)

A servant girl came and recognised Peter.
She said, 'That man Jesus, he is your leader.'
But Peter, he panicked and hotly denied:
'Woman you're crazy. He's not!' he cried.
The Rock.

(Servant girl steps back into chorus. Another steps forward as Man 1 and folds arms, looking at Peter, who turns his face away.)

A little while later a man in the crowd,
Recognised Peter and spoke out loud.
'You, you are one of them – one of his lot.'
'Man, I know nothing. No I am not.'
The Rock.

(Man 1 steps back. Man 2 steps forward and gestures strongly. Peter turns towards him, looking angry.)

About an hour later, another stepped near:
'This man is from Galilee. Look at him here.
He was with Jesus – no shadow of doubt.'
'Man, I don't know what you're talking about.'
The Rock.

(Peter goes out of the circle and puts his head in his hands.)

Peter went out and cried, all alone.
Peter remembered that Jesus had known.
'You will deny that you know me tonight.'
He was a failure: Jesus was right.
The Rock?

(The chorus is silent, with heads bowed. The narrator continues, not in verse.)

They took Jesus away and crucified him. When he was dead, some of his followers came and buried him. But two days later, the tomb was empty. Jesus was alive again and the disciples met and talked with him. Then, one day, Peter and the others went out fishing just as they used to before they met Jesus.

51

(Chorus become a group of fishermen, sitting in a boat holding a net over the side. They begin 'Rock Rock Rockety Rock' again as the boat rocks on the lake.)

NARRATOR: (*in verse*)
They fished through the night but caught nothing at all.
At dawn, from the lakeside, they heard a voice call:
'Throw out your nets over there – on the right.'
The moment they cast them, the nets were filled tight.
The Rock.

(One of the chorus points to shore. Peter jumps out and starts wading through water.)

One of them cried out: 'It's the Lord!'
Peter looked up and then jumped overboard.
Jesus cooked breakfast and gave each a share.
Peter was happy now Jesus was there.
The Rock.

(Chorus stop the chant and sit in a group on the shore, sharing food. Peter walks away from them and stands as if talking with Jesus.)

NARRATOR: After breakfast, Jesus said to Peter, 'Simon, son of John, do you love me more than these others do?'
PETER: Yes, Lord, you know that I love you.
NARRATOR: Take care of my lambs. Simon, son of John, do you love me?
PETER: Yes, Lord, you know that I love you.
NARRATOR: Take care of my sheep. Simon, son of John, do you love me?
PETER: Lord, you know everything; you know that I love you!
NARRATOR: Take care of my sheep. When you are old you will stretch out your hands and someone will bind you and take you where you do not want to go.

(Chorus begin to chant again. During this verse, Peter returns to the chorus/disciples. They greet each other, then Peter beckons the others and they go off chatting excitedly together.)

Peter the Rock, *was* Jesus' friend.
Ready to stick with him, right to the end.
Peter was changed, forgiven and free.
And he never forgot Jesus' words: 'Follow me.'
The Rock.

Instant pose

Bible base: Acts 1:6-11; 2:1-4,43-47

This is a role-play activity. Read Acts 1:6-11 and Acts 2:1-4,43-47 with your group. Divide the group into smaller groups of four or five and give each group one of the passages. Tell them that you want them to form a 'photograph' for their passage. They must decide who is going to act which character, and then freeze in a group pose which reflects what is happening in the passage.

Suggestions could be:

Acts 1:6-9: Disciples staring up to heaven, looking gobsmacked, waving, mouths wide open.

Acts 1:10,11: Disciples meeting angels, looking startled and worried.

Acts 2:1-4: Disciples swept off feet, hanging on to furniture as wind overtakes and engulfs them. Disciples point at one another in amazement.

Acts 2:43-47 Disciples performing miracles, praising, caring, much more confident.

Discussion starter:

Take the four 'photos' in turn, allowing everyone to see each group pose. What was the difference between the first and last photo? What caused this change? Explain that it was the Holy Spirit who transformed the disciples from feeling scared and despondent to joyful and confident.

Foiled again!

HUGH BOORMAN  2

Bible base: Acts 1:12–14; 4:23–31

Cast

'**ONE**' and '**TWO**', dressed like secret agents with dark glasses, long raincoats with turned-up collars, and each wearing a hat to conceal much of their head.

'One' and 'Two' are acting furtively, looking down and observing the apostles from afar.

ONE: Well, Two, I think we've got them this time. We've really put Peter and John through it.

TWO: Don't be so sure, One. We thought that we'd beaten them last time, didn't we, when we had Jesus arrested and executed on some trumped-up charge?

ONE: Yeah, that really put the wind up them! The apostles were scattered for miles. Heh, heh!

TWO: Yes, but they gathered together again, didn't they? Even when he was taken up to heaven, that didn't stop them. They kept meeting and praying together.

ONE: Yeah, but this is different. Now we're actually giving them the problems, aren't we?

TWO: (*Rubbing his hands together*) Yes. Heh, heh, heh!

ONE: Think about it... We've had Peter and John arrested, thrown into jail, interrogated and threatened. If that hasn't silenced them, nothing will. Heh, heh!

TWO: You're right. They wouldn't dare to say anything now.

ONE: Shh! Look, they've been released and have got back with the others. What are they up to?

TWO: Looks like they're about to pray. Let's hear them squeal with fear to their God.

ONE: Hang on a minute! They're not squealing. What are they doing?

TWO: They're praising God. They're asking him to use them more. We haven't silenced them at all.

ONE: No. They seem to be even more enthusiastic than before. What's wrong with them?

TWO: It's that secret weapon of theirs again, isn't it? We don't stand a chance while they keep on using it.

ONE: What?

TWO: Their prayers together. You see, God answers them.

ONE: Curses! Foiled again!

Jigsaw tale

TRICIA YON

Bible base: Acts 3:1–10

Cast
FIVE READERS who each read a line at a time.

ONE: One day
TWO: One fine day
THREE: One beautiful day
FOUR: One beautifully fine day
FIVE: Peter and John
ONE: Went to the temple
TWO: At
THREE: Three o'clock
FOUR: Precisely.
FIVE: There at the
ONE: Gate
TWO: A very fine gate
THREE: A beautiful gate
FOUR: A beautifully fine gate
FIVE: Sat
ONE: Begging and pleading
TWO: Pleading and begging
THREE: Avoiding the eyes of
FOUR: The passers-by of
FIVE: The beautiful gate
ONE: Stretching his hands out
TWO: And hoping for silver
THREE: Or gold
FOUR: (*Interrupting*) Or Visa or American Express
FIVE: Whatever they'd got
ONE: In their pockets or purses
TWO: Sat
THREE: A man
FOUR: A man lame from birth
FIVE: Whose friends
ONE: (*Interrupting*) Some friends!
TWO: Carried him daily
THREE: And left him to wait
FOUR: At the beautiful gate
FIVE: Until Peter and John and others just like them
ONE: Passed by.
TWO: And then, the man
THREE: With the friends
FOUR: Who left him
FIVE: Would call out for money, or
ONE: Whatever.

TWO: But Peter and John
THREE: Had no money to give.
FOUR: Peter and John
FIVE: Felt bad.
ONE: Peter and John knew
TWO: Something better could
THREE: Help
FOUR: The man
FIVE: With the friends
ONE: Who left
TWO: (*Interrupting*) Get on with it!
THREE: Peter and John
FOUR: Remembered
FIVE: How Jesus
ONE: Could heal
TWO: The blind
THREE: The sick
FOUR: The paralysed
FIVE: And any others who came to him and believed and trusted and did as Jesus said.
ONE: So Peter and John
TWO: Said
THREE: 'Sorry mate
FOUR: No dosh
FIVE: But
ONE: Just look at us and
TWO: Concentrate
THREE: On Jesus
FOUR: His name
FIVE: His power
ONE: And get up!
TWO: Get up
THREE: And
FOUR: Walk!'
FIVE: Then Peter took him
ONE: By the hand…
TWO: (*Interrupting*) Right or left?
THREE: Then Peter took him
FOUR: By the right hand
FIVE: And…
ONE: Wait for it…
TWO: Drum roll…
THREE: Fanfare…
FOUR: Sharp intake of breath…
FIVE: Peter

ONE: Helped him up.
TWO: Did he fall?
THREE: Nope.
FOUR: Did he stagger?
FIVE: Nope.
ONE: Was.he hypnotised?
TWO: Nope.
THREE: He stood up.
FOUR: Right on his feet.
FIVE: His feet
ONE: And
TWO: His ankles
THREE: Became
FOUR: Strong. Pow!
FIVE: That would be enough
ONE: For most men
TWO: I would say.
THREE: Hear, hear!
FOUR: But for this man
FIVE: This lame man
ONE: With the friends
TWO: Who
THREE: Left him each day

FOUR: At the gate which
FIVE: Was fine and beautiful
ONE: Or beautifully fine
TWO: This wasn't enough
THREE: Not nearly enough.
FOUR: He jumped
FIVE: Up and down
ONE: And round and round
TWO: Shouting
THREE: And praising…
FOUR: Peter and John?
FIVE: No!
ONE: Friends and neighbours?
TWO: No!
THREE: Then who?
FOUR: Jumping and
FIVE: Walking and
ONE: Praising God!
TWO: Who
THREE: Had healed him
FOUR: In Jesus' name.
FIVE: Wow!

A red letter day

Bible base: Acts 18:18-23; 19:20-22; 20:1,2

This scripted story is a conversation between Aquila and Priscilla. After the first few lines, it can be read, using a copy of the script as the letter from Paul.

PRISCILLA: Aquila! Aquila! Come here, there's a letter from Paul.

AQUILA: Well, what does he say?

PRISCILLA: How should I know? I haven't opened it yet.

AQUILA: Oh, give it here. *(Takes letter.)*

PRISCILLA: *(She snatches it away and opens it.)* Paul, a servant of Christ Jesus. To… *(Reads silently.)*

AQUILA: Well, tell me then.

PRISCILLA: He's been visiting all the new Christians in Macedonia. It's very exciting.

AQUILA: Well, read it out to me, then.

PRISCILLA: *(Reads.)* I have been visiting all the new Christians in Macedonia.

AQUILA: *(Snatches letter and reads. Priscilla looks over his shoulder and comments.)* … and there are lots of new believers in Macedonia, too.

PRISCILLA: That's wonderful!

AQUILA: Now I am in Corinth.

PRISCILLA: It's taken him long enough to get there.

AQUILA: My feet hurt from walking, but that is nothing compared to the joy of serving God.

PRISCILLA: He doesn't change. Is he staying at our old place in Corinth? They were good times, working there.

AQUILA: Things have been difficult for the church here in Corinth.

PRISCILLA: Oh dear!

AQUILA: I wanted to sail straight on to Jerusalem, but there is a plot against me, so I will have to go back through Macedonia.

PRISCILLA: Oh, poor Paul! Does that mean he'll come back here to Ephesus?

AQUILA: I hope to meet up with the leaders from Ephesus somewhere, but I must keep going.

PRISCILLA: Why? I know people need to hear the good news, but couldn't he come here for a holiday?

AQUILA: I must go on to Jerusalem, and then I am sure God wants me to travel to Rome. Please pray for the churches, and that people will listen to me and believe in Jesus.

PRISCILLA: I don't understand him. He's been travelling all this time - he's been swamped in rivers, attacked by bandits, shipwrecked, gone without food and water and I don't know what else - and he still only asks us to pray for people to believe in Jesus. It's all he cares about.

AQUILA: Come on, Priscilla, let's pray for him now. *(They leave.)*

Discussion starter: Afterwards, look at Acts 19:21,22 together. Use the map if you have one to show the journeys Paul was planning to make. Read out 2 Corinthians 11:24-28 to show what travelling was like. Paul thought the hardship was worth it. People heard the good news and the churches were strengthened.

Trouble on site †

CATHIE BARTLAM

Bible base: Ephesians 2:20–22

Cast
NARRATOR
MASTER BUILDER
THE STONE FAMILY
MISS SG WINDOW
MRS FOUNDATION
MR DOOR
DR ROOF

Props and costumes: a square marked out on the floor with tape; two chairs or stepladders; a grey blanket; Master Builder wears a hard hat and carries a set of plans; the Stone family are dressed completely in one colour, eg grey, brown or white; Miss SG Window is dressed in very colourful clothes including a large hat; Mrs Foundation wears grey all over; Mr Door should carry a handle and a battery-operated doorbell; Dr Roof is dressed completely in waterproof clothing including boots and hat, and carrying an umbrella and a couple of newspapers.

The scene is a building site.

NARRATOR: Once upon a time, a master builder decided to construct a wonderful church. It was going to be the best he could build. He spent a lot of time getting everything ready. All the steel and cement was ready for the foundations. (*Enter Mrs Foundation.*) The stones were cut to size. (*Enter the Stone family who make a heap on one side.*) The door had been polished and fitted with a bell. (*Enter Mr Door smiling and ringing his bell.*) The roofing trusses were prepared and all the slates in place. (*Enter Dr Roof twirling an umbrella.*) And last of all, the beautiful stained glass window was finished. (*Enter Miss SG Window, like a catwalk model, who walks and twirls, walks and twirls.*)

MASTER BUILDER: I can get on with building the church. I'm so excited. All the preparations are done. I've dug a huge hole, so now it's time for you. (*Points to Mrs Foundation.*)

MRS FOUNDATION: Me?

MASTER BUILDER: Yes, you, Foundation. Your moment has arrived.

MRS FOUNDATION: At last. This is what I've been waiting for.

MASTER BUILDER: Good. Please go and lie down in the hole.

MRS FOUNDATION: (*Disbelievingly*) In the hole?

MASTER BUILDER: Yes.

MRS FOUNDATION: But I'll get dirty!

MASTER BUILDER: Of course.

MRS FOUNDATION: And I won't be able to see what's going on.

MASTER BUILDER: True. But don't worry, most people won't even know you're there.

MRS FOUNDATION: Won't know I'm there?

MASTER BUILDER: Well, not after you're covered with a layer of concrete. (*Mrs Foundation tries to run away*) Hey! Where are you going?

MRS FOUNDATION: I'm off. No one told me about the concrete.

MASTER BUILDER: But that's what you're there for. You are the foundations, aren't you?

MRS FOUNDATION: Yes, but...

MASTER BUILDER: ... and a lot of time and energy and money have gone into making you.

MRS FOUNDATION: But...

MASTER BUILDER: So, now I want you to get into place.

MRS FOUNDATION: I don't want to!

MASTER BUILDER: Don't want to?

MRS FOUNDATION: You see, I didn't think I'd be hidden away. I knew I was going to be a big part of the church, a very big part.

MASTER BUILDER: Very big.

MRS FOUNDATION: But I didn't think I'd be hidden away. I don't like it at all. I thought everyone would look at me, and... and...

MASTER BUILDER: Think how marvellous you are?

MRS FOUNDATION: (*Drops head.*) Well, yes.

MASTER BUILDER: But Foundation, you *are* marvellous. Without you, we can't go on.

MRS FOUNDATION: Really?

MASTER BUILDER: The church can't be built. You are vital.

MRS FOUNDATION: But everyone will forget about me.

MASTER BUILDER: Probably, unless they need to

drill through for a new pipe or check your damp-proofing. I think it is true that hardly anyone will know you exist. (*Pause*)

MRS FOUNDATION: And you really want me to do it?

MASTER BUILDER: If you would.

MRS FOUNDATION: I don't understand, but you're the master builder, you're the one with the plans. I'll do whatever you want. (*Mrs Foundation lies down and is covered with a grey blanket.*)

MASTER BUILDER: Right. Stones next.

STONE FAMILY: Oh goody. (*Lots of shoving and pushing as the Stone family make a wall.*) Move over! Get your elbow out of my back. You've put on weight. Hey, squeeze in here. (*Master Builder makes a gap for the door. Mr Door ambles up.*)

MISS SG WINDOW: (*Interrupting*) This is ridiculous.

MASTER BUILDER: Ridiculous?

MISS SG WINDOW: All this fuss over some boring brown and grey lumps. Have you any idea how much I'm worth, how much I can earn in a day, modelling?

MASTER BUILDER: Not really.

MISS SG WINDOW: And you keep me hanging about here while you discuss life and the universe with Foundation, who you've now buried, and we watch the antics of these Stones!

MASTER BUILDER: They're essential. Without them we're lost.

MISS SG WINDOW: Essential! They are drab, boring and don't seem to have a working brain cell between them. (*Mr Door rings his bell.*) What are you doing?

MR DOOR: Just checking my batteries.

MISS SG WINDOW: Idiot! You're the master builder, just get on with it.

MASTER BUILDER: With what?

MISS SG WINDOW: With me! I'm the centre of this building. It's at me all will look and gasp and wonder; at me the cameras will flash; at me that the sun will bend its rays to send coloured patterns of light over my adoring fans.

MASTER BUILDER: But I can't put you in place yet. You have to wait. The stones, the walls, the windows, the roof - all these must be finished first. You just have a cup of tea and be patient.

MISS SG WINDOW: Patient! Tea! I don't think you know who you are talking to. I demand action now.

MASTER BUILDER: (*Quietly and calmly*) Okay. Stained glass window, would you kindly get into position, two metres up on the north side of the building.

MISS SG WINDOW: What north side?

MASTER BUILDER: That's where you are made to go. (*Miss SG Window goes to the far side of the taped square where there are no stones and starts leaping into the air trying to get two metres off the ground. Master Builder takes out a long tape measure and attempts to measure her jumps.*) Only 45 centimetres on that one. Tut, tut.

MISS SG WINDOW: I'll do it!

MASTER BUILDER: 75 centimetres - any advance on that? (*Stained Glass Window shrugs her shoulders and walks off.*)

MR DOOR: She seems a bit worked-up, sir.

MASTER BUILDER: A bit. She'll calm down eventually.

MR DOOR: Why don't you tell her off?

MASTER BUILDER: Because I made her. Stained Glass Window is very special, but so are all of you.

MR DOOR: But she is so much more beautiful than me.

MASTER BUILDER: Just believe me, each one of you is special. Look at Roof. (*He points to Dr Roof sitting on a chair, reading a paper very patiently.*) She could learn a few things from him. He's just waiting until the time is right to be put into place.

MR DOOR: What will happen to Stained Glass Window, sir?

MASTER BUILDER: She'll learn the hard way. You see, actually she won't be put into place until everything else is done.

MR DOOR: In fact, we could do without her, couldn't we, sir?

MASTER BUILDER: No, Door. She's part of my building, my church, but she needs to learn that she is only a part.

MRS FOUNDATION: (*Muffled*) Is anyone going to build on me?

STONE FAMILY: Me! Me! (*Stone family reform in a neat line behind covered Foundation. Door then moves steadily into place. Roof gets out another magazine.*)

MASTER BUILDER: Roof, time for you now. Are the waterproofs okay?

DR ROOF: Very good, sir. (*Climbs on wooden block or stepladder and holds out his arms.*) What about… you know… her, sir?

(*Master Builder walks round, inspects the site, prods a few stones into place, consults his plans and puts a block or stepladder on the end.*)

MASTER BUILDER: We're ready. (*He goes out and returns with Stained Glass Window walking quietly and calmly.*) Would you please get into position? (*Stained Glass Window climbs on to the block or stepladder. Door smiles and rings his bell. All stay in place.*)

NARRATOR: 'You are like a building with the apostles and prophets as the foundation and with Christ as the most important stone. Christ is the one who holds the building together and makes it grow into a holy temple for the Lord. And you are part of that building Christ has built as a place for God's own Spirit to live.'

(Ephesians 2:20-22 CEV).

Index

Titles (alphabetical order)

A circular drama 20
A job well done! 25
All God's plan 9
A red letter day 57
Crossed lines 30
David, the giant-killer! 14
Elijah finds God 17
Fired up! 23
Foiled again! 54
Follow the Leader .33
Get ready for Jesus 26
Going potty! 22
Gumpole of the Bailey 49
Instant pose 53
In the beginning, God... 6
Jigsaw tale 55
Lots of action 8
Malchus' miracle .46
Manasseh changes 21
Nehemiah builds a wall 24
On the record 29
On the run 15
P-R-O-P-H-E-T 19
Rockety Rock 51
Sheep tales 41
Shocking! 40
Sidney Spender, Super Spender 42
The big fight 31
The king acts 11
The perfect prayer 38
There's some wine in my bucket! 36
They're gone 16
Trouble on site 58
Two a penny 39
Wait till I tell you! 44
Walk through story 12
What a scoop! 48
What a surprise! .28
Words of hope 27
Zebedee phones home 35

Themes (alphabetical order)

Christmas
Gabriel visits Mary 27
Joseph's dream .28
The birth of Jesus 29
The visit of the wise men 30
Zechariah's prophecy about John 26

Easter
Easter Sunday 48, 49
Palm Sunday 44
The arrest of Jesus 46
The Marys find the empty tomb 48
The resurrection .49

Life of Jesus
John the Baptist prepares for Jesus 26
Calling of first disciples 33, 35
Jesus and the children 40
Jesus calls the fishermen 35
Parable of the unforgiving servant 42
The Ascension 53
The call of James and John 35
The first miracle .36
The lost sheep 41
The story of the sparrows 39
The temptations .31
Wedding at Cana 36

Old Testament
Creation 6
Abraham and Lot separate 8
Abraham rescues Lot 8
Crossing of the Red Sea 12
Daniel's friends obey God 23
David and Goliath 14
David escapes from Gath 15
David mourns Saul and Jonathan 16
Elijah: famine and meeting God 17
Jeremiah's parable of the potter 22
Joash restores the temple 20
Joseph 9
Manasseh turns to God 21
Moses: The Passover 12
Moses and Pharaoh 11
Nehemiah rebuilds Jerusalem's walls 24
Nehemiah's work completed 25
Prophets 19
The fiery furnace 23

Prayer
God answers 54
The Lord's Prayer 38

INDEXES

The Church

God's building 58
Paul's journeys 57
Pentecost 53
Peter and John arrested 54
Peter and John heal a man 55
Peter's denial 51
The believers face persecution 54
The healing at the beautiful Gate 55
The living building 58

Bible passages

Genesis 1, 2	In the beginning God…
Genesis 13:1–18;	
14:1–16	Lots of action
Genesis 37, 39–46	All God's plan
Exodus 1:1 – 2:10	The king acts
Exodus 12:21–36;	
13:17 – 14:31	Walk through story
1 Samuel 17:1–58	David, the giant-killer!
1 Samuel 21:10 – 22:4	On the run
2 Samuel 1:1–27	They're gone
1 Kings 18:16–46	P-R-O-P-H-E-T
1 Kings 19:1–15	Elijah finds God
2 Kings 5	P-R-O-P-H-E-T
2 Chronicles 24:1–16	A circular drama
2 Chronicles 33:1–20	Manasseh changes
Nehemiah 4	Nehemiah builds a wall; A job well done!
Nehemiah 6:15,16	Nehemiah builds a wall; A job well done!
Jeremiah 18:1–12	Going potty!
Daniel 2,4,5	P-R-O-P-H-E-T
Daniel 3:1–30	Fired up!
Jonah 1–3	P-R-O-P-H-E-T
Zechariah 9:9	Wait till I tell you!
Matthew 1:18–25	What a surprise!
Matthew 2:1–12	Crossed lines
Matthew 4:18–25	Zebedee phones home
Matthew 10:29–31	Two a penny!

Matthew 18:1-5	Shocking!
Matthew 18:10-14	Sheep tales
Matthew 18:21-35	Sidney Spender, Super Spender
Matthew 19:13-15	Shocking!
Matthew 26:47-56	Malchus' miracle
Matthew 27:62-66	Gumpole of the Bailey
Matthew 28:1-10	What a scoop!
Matthew 28:11-15	Gumpole of the Bailey
Luke 1:26-45	Words of hope
Luke 1:67-80	Get ready for Jesus
Luke 2:1-7	On the record
Luke 3:1-18	Get ready for Jesus
Luke 4:1-13	The big fight
Luke 5:1-8	Follow the Leader
Luke 11:1-4	The perfect prayer
John 2:1-12	There's some wine in my bucket!
John 12:12-16	Wait till I tell you!
John 18:15-18,	
25-27; 21:15-25	Rockety Rock
Acts 1:6-11	Instant pose
Acts 1:12-14	Foiled again!
Acts 2:1-4,43-47	Instant pose
Acts 3:1-10	Jigsaw tale
Acts 4:23-31	Foiled again!
Acts 18:18-23;	
19:20-22; 20:1,2	A red letter day
Ephesians 2:20-22	Trouble on site

Resources from
Scripture Union

Drama

Oh no, not the Nativity! Sketches through the church year
Andrew Brandon et al

Looking for inspiration as Christmas/Easter/ Harvest comes round again? This is an original collection of over 20 mini-plays and monologues, using poetry, humour and serious drama to take a fresh look at key events in Jesus' life and mark other special occasions in the church year.
ISBN 1 85999 233 1 £6.99

Get a Life! Sketches for your youth group
Farrow, Sands, Bower

A collection of 15 thematic, Bible-based sketches for youth groups to perform themselves.
Exploring a range of topical issues, this is a valuable resource for your youth group!
ISBN 1 85999 232 3 £6.99

Rap, Rhyme and Reason
Anita Haigh

A collection of monologues, poems, sketches and raps based on Jesus' teaching, to perform in schools, youth groups and family services.
ISBN 1 85999 036 3 £4.99

Resources for children's group leaders

Here's One I Made Earlier: Scripture Union craft resources for 3s to 11s
Compiled by Kathryn Copsey

Designed for use with 3 to 11 year olds, this wide-ranging collection of craft activities features 16 categories of crafts linked to Bible stories, with pictures, puppets, models, mobiles and many more.
ISBN 0 86201 981 8 £7.99

Here's Another One I Made Earlier: Scripture Union craft resources for 3s to 11s
Compiled by Christine Orme

The follow-up to the tremendously successful *Here's One I Made Earlier*.
Arranged thematically for easy reference, this resource provides craft activities on subjects such as Advent, Christmas, Mothering Sunday, Easter, Prayer, God's world, and many more…
ISBN 9 781859 993385 £7.99

Theme Games
Lesley Pinchbeck

With around 150 games arranged thematically and well-indexed, you should always be able to find the right game to link in with your programme.
ISBN 0 86201 841 2
£5.99

Over 300 Games for All Occasions
Compiled by Patrick Goodland

A revised edition of this popular handbook including outdoor games for groups, canopy and parachute games, fun games with balloons, party games and much much more. A brand new section includes games for travelling, whether by plane, train or car.
ISBN 1 85999 264 1 £6.99

Quiz Resource Book
Richard and Mary Chewter

This easy-to-use guide to quizzes is ideal for group leaders who are short of time or fresh ideas. It provides drawings and diagrams, ready to use quizzes and help in creating and presenting your own.
ISBN 1 85999 049 5 £7.50

Pick 'n' Mix: Over 100 ideas to create programmes for children of all ages!
Judith Merrell

An excellent resource for children's leaders, containing ideas for icebreakers, ways of telling Bible stories, quizzes, crafts, games and creative prayers.
1 85999 096 7 £6.99

Growing in Faith series
These books work together, providing a 'head, heart and hands' approach to the subject of child faith development. Written by experts in their field, the series will equip churches with a comprehensive training resource for children's workers.

Children Finding Faith: Exploring a child's response to God
Francis Bridger

In this revised and updated version of his prize-winning book, Francis Bridger looks at the ways in which children develop physically, mentally and emotionally from birth to adolescence and shows how these insights can help us share the gospel more effectively with them.
ISBN 1 85999 323 0 £6.99

Bringing Children to Faith: Training adults in evangelism with children
Penny Frank

With photocopiable resources and suggestions for group discussion and activity, this is an ideal training resource for your church children's team. Use it to plan a series of workshops or develop a whole-church strategy for children's evangelism.
ISBN 1 85999 410 5 £7.50

Mission Possible: Ideas and resources for children's evangelism
Compiled by David Bell and Rachel Heathfield

A ready-to-use resource packed with tried and tested ideas for children's evangelism.
ISBN 1 85999 411 3 £7.50

Ordering resources

All of these resources can be obtained from your local Christian bookshop or direct from the address below. Alternatively, order online through www.christianbookshop.com

For more information about resources from Scripture Union visit our website: www.scriptureunion.org.uk

ISBN	TITLE	QUANTITY	PRICE (each)	PRICE (total)

		TOTAL COST OF GOODS	
		Postage & Packing	
		Donation to Scripture Union	
		TOTAL ENCLOSED	

When ordering, please include ISBN, title, quantity and price.
All titles subject to availability.
Prices subject to change without notice.

Ordering Information

Please complete the payment details below.

All orders must be accompanied by the appropriate payment.

Send this completed form to:

Scripture Union Mail Order
PO Box 5148
Milton Keynes MLO
MK2 2YX
Tel: 01908 856006 Fax: 01908 856020
subs@scriptureunion.org.uk

Postage and Packing Rates

Order Value	UK	Europe	Rest of World Surface	Rest of World Airmail
£6.00 & under	£1.25	£2.25	£2.25	£3.50
£6.01-14.99	£3.00	£3.50	£4.50	£6.00
£15.00-29.99	£4.00	£5.50	£7.50	£11.00
£30.00 & over	FREE	PRICE ON REQUEST		

Ordered by

Mrs/Mr/Miss/Ms/Revd

Address

Postcode

Daytime tel

Email

(for any query about your order)

Delivery address (if different)

Mrs/Mr/Miss/Ms/Revd

Address

Postcode

Daytime tel

(for any query about your order)

Payment Details

Method of Payment: ☐ Cheque*   ☐ Mastercard   ☐ Visa   ☐ Switch   ☐ Postal order*

Credit card number: ☐☐☐☐ ☐☐☐☐ ☐☐☐☐ ☐☐☐☐   Expiry Date: ☐☐☐☐

Switch card number: ☐☐☐☐☐☐☐☐☐☐☐☐☐☐☐☐☐☐   Expiry Date: ☐☐☐☐

Issue number of Switch card: ☐☐☐

Signature:

(necessary if payment by credit card)

Date:

*made payable to Scripture Union

Please print name which appears on credit card:

Please print the address the card is billed to, if different from above:

RESOURCES FROM SCRIPTURE UNION